PUZZLE 3

ACROSS

1 Without (Ger.)
5 Put up to
11 "— Purple" (1939 song)
12 Mariners
13 Gaelic
14 Doting
15 Kane's sled
17 Thrice (Lat.)
18 Spanish for king
19 Gaucho's country (abbr.)
20 Highway
22 Tarry
23 Pavilion
24 Espied
25 Cupola
26 Germ
27 Onassis
28 Billy — Williams
29 Negative
30 Famed conductor
35 Indian city
37 O'Hara plantation
38 Interpose
39 Elliptical
40 One of the Manns
41 Baseball's Rose

DOWN

1 European river
2 Brave one
3 Stack TV role
4 Fencing foil
5 Published
6 In want
7 Preserve
8 Copied
9 Aircraft navigation system
10 Vim
16 Enfant terrible
20 Memorandum
21 United
22 Get it?
23 Canadian city
24 Appear
25 — pastry
26 Untroubled
28 Architectural style
31 On
32 Cathedral section
33 Doggone!
34 Harvard's rival
36 W.W.II org.

KT-469-385

PUZZLE 4

ACROSS

1 Strike-breaker
5 Film critic
10 Remark upon
11 "My Cousin —"
13 One of the Ages
14 Expand the lungs
15 Sicilian city
17 Throw
18 Cloth measure
19 Adverb, to odists
20 Indefinite period
21 Vast area
22 Apartment
23 Charger
26 Noted "Duke"
27 Soviet lake
28 Roll of bills
29 Us (Sp.)
30 Knightly title
31 Háw. food
34 Egyptian king
35 Audrey —
37 One kind of band
39 Ardor
40 Altercation
41 Noble Italian name
42 Register
43 Nobleman

DOWN

1 Game bird
2 Deep pink
3 Ring-shaped island
4 Nota —
5 Russian resort
6 Talked, talked, talked
7 German I
8 Like Miss America
9 Aircraft navigation system
12 Emissary
16 College in Oregon
21 Salt (Fr.)
22 Craze
23 Brazilian seaport
24 Pommel
25 Of the Orient
26 Distort
28 Cyber-netics pioneer
30 Form
31 Throb
32 Deliver an address
33 Spiritual
36 Electronic sound
38 Covering

4

PUZZLE 1

ACROSS

1 Map; plot
5 Swedish man's name
9 Learning
10 Spellbinder
13 Brazilian tapir
14 Conduct oneself
15 Assuredly
16 At — (lost)
17 Young merino
18 Senior citizenry
20 S.A. republic
21 Mideast money
23 Drumbeat
24 — rubber
25 Capital of Bulgaria
26 Religious body
27 Penetrate
28 Goes wrong
29 Expensive
30 One — time
31 Apiece
32 Man's name
35 Screened
37 Resting place
38 At the table
39 Italian river
40 Surfeit
41 Collar style

DOWN

1 Horse around
2 Desolate
3 School course
4 "— and Sympathy"
5 Lobate
6 Region
7 Cheerful shout
8 Like some computers
11 Reach across
12 Habitual
16 Evening, in Messina
19 Paces
20 Fork part
21 Affliction
22 Sluggishness
25 Israel mtn. region
29 Quibble
31 Confined
33 Port. measure
34 Gold club
36 Aunt (Sp.)
37 New Guinea town

1

PUZZLE 2

ACROSS
1 Lummox
5 Barber's item
10 — and hair
11 Drive
13 Egyptian deity
14 "Ivanhoe" lady
15 Welsh delicacy
17 Traitor
18 Aver anew
20 Golda —
22 "Have you got change of —?"
23 Jalopy
25 American poet
26 Of aircraft
27 Break-water
28 Brought out
30 You (Ger.)
31 Irregularity
36 Direction on ship
38 Norma's "Casta Diva"
39 Go to bed
40 Word to a broker
41 Challenged

42 Detest

DOWN
1 Burn
2 Ohio city
3 Repute
4 Dune
5 Less lazy
6 Riding paces
7 Falling out

8 Switch-board worker
9 Roman deities
12 Hidden
16 French cheese
19 Biblical weed

20 Georgia city
21 Jacket style
23 Early TV favorite
24 Emended
25 Dog's name
27 Wrote

29 Novelist John le —
32 Pulverize
33 Scope
34 Cadence
35 Merriwell's school
37 Norse goddess

2

PUZZLE 5

ACROSS

1 Top of the head
5 Kate of song
10 Grandparental
11 Laundry appliance
13 Depend
14 Hold fast
15 Exasperate
16 "There — Such Things"
17 Margaret, to friends
18 Laid away
20 "I never — man I never liked"
21 Long-distance
22 Seed coating
23 Maxene, La Verne and —
25 Myth. enchantress
26 Throb
27 "— Wednesday"
28 Frosted
29 Yarn
32 Inflexible
33 Arid
34 Asian river
35 Renee —
37 Blue-pencil
38 Most original
39 By —
40 Moccasin is one
41 Pitcher

DOWN

1 Helen's abductor
2 Ward off
3 Grant film (1942)
4 District of England
5 Turf
6 Created
7 Somewhat (suff.)
8 Lehar operetta
9 Apostate
12 Treat festively
16 Lofty nest
19 Deserved
20 Famed battleship
23 Rossellini film (1947)
24 Consents
25 — Grant
29 Medit. island
30 Type size
31 Liquid measure
33 "The — Set" (1956 film)
36 Turmeric
37 Before

5

PUZZLE 6

ACROSS
1 Raven
5 Refreshed
11 Nevada city
12 Lie down
13 Arabian city
14 Sagacious
15 Network
16 Suffix
17 Lenin's program of 1921 (abbr.)
18 MGM's lion
19 Fixed
20 — Aviv
21 Brice's big song
23 Host
24 Tempura sauce
25 Curve in ship's timber
26 — au rhum
28 Subsequently
30 Timorese coin
31 Intimate
32 Table scrap
34 Suffers from
35 Wholly
36 Suffix

37 Hamburg's port
39 Bavarian river
40 Pipe-dreamed
41 Scottish waterfall
42 Chronicle
43 Before (Lat.)

DOWN
1 Grovel

2 Take out of pawn
3 Adm. Morison's best seller
4 Gained
5 Impudent
6 Adjust anew
7 Fit
8 Rustic relative
9 Respect

10 With emotion
16 Really!
22 Extinct bird
23 Girl's name
25 Doorway feature
26 — Islands off Florida

27 Legendary paradise
28 Leafy dishes
29 Wandering
31 Jury list
33 Lead-tin alloy
38 — dare
39 Dock-workers union

6

PUZZLE 7

ACROSS

1 Pornography
5 Perkins and Barker
8 "Mr. Deeds" director
10 Wrongly
13 Playful trick
14 Because
15 Old auto
16 Chinese pagoda
18 "El —"
19 Ruth's mother-in-law
21 Pasture
22 "Barber of Seville" heroine
24 Insincere talk
25 Sheeplike
26 Dr. Phibes in films
27 Hunter's shelter
28 Blow one's top
29 Circle segment
30 Of current affairs
31 Chess champion (1960-61)
32 Partook of
33 Greek letter
36 Russian stockade
38 Let down, as a window
40 Follower of deism
41 Type size
42 Inlet (Sp.)
43 On water

DOWN

1 Capone feature
2 Neck hair
3 Lanny Budd's creator
4 Prefix with cycle
5 An African people
6 Friend, in Toulon
7 Babbitt's creator
9 Moss Hart work
11 — fiction
12 Calmed
17 Candlenut tree
20 "— We Got Fun"
22 Revolved
23 Went off the diet
24 Actor Joel Mc—
26 Hawk
28 New Mex. Indian
30 Greek letter
34 Head (Fr.)
35 Field
37 Greek letter
39 Palm leaf

PUZZLE 8

ACROSS

1 Bristles
5 Woe unto us!
9 Wild goat
10 Medieval cloth
13 Famous film critic
14 Like some kisses
15 Torme
16 Alkali
17 Old soldier
18 Acquire
20 Greek letter
21 Political cartoonist
22 Three (Ger.)
23 Ringlet
25 Award
26 Steak preference
27 Appetite stimulant
28 Marsh plant
29 Singer Barry
32 Storage place
33 Cheer in Cadiz
34 Gibbon
35 Fine wool
37 Pharaoh
38 Cast certain glances
39 Editor's mark
40 Trust
41 Helot

DOWN

1 Terence —
2 Anxious
3 Role for Clayton Moore
4 "Chances —"
5 Affirm
6 Shaping machine
7 I love (Lat.)
8 Reminders of 3 Down
11 Squirrel monkey
12 Require
16 — Columbo
19 Example
22 East Indian boat
23 Of a nomadic people
24 Narrow valley
25 English river
27 Affliction
29 Mushroom
30 Composed of cereal
31 Indite
36 Miner's find
37 Compass reading

8

PUZZLE 9

ACROSS
1 Parlor piece
5 Maxim
10 Golf club
11 Simpletons
13 Surrealist painter
14 Completely
15 Building wing
16 Cozy room
17 Large vase
18 Think
20 "—and Sympathy"
21 One kind of cheese
22 Castle feature
23 Stylish
24 Not— finger (not help)
25 Chanticleer
26 Odious
27 Winnie-the-Pooh friend
28 House feature
29 Babylonian deity
30 "Pride— Prejudice"
31 A Gabor
34 Corsair
36 Take a dip
37 Sword-shaped
38 Alleviate
39 Icy
40 "—'s Daughter"

DOWN
1 Faction
2 Spoken
3 Go directly
4 Black cuckoo
5 French city
6 English poet
7 Skill
8 Make an effort
9 Prayer
12 Musical work
16 D.J.'s platter
19 "The— Panther"
21 Fainting
22 Sundry (abbr.)
23 Abrade
24 Fat
26 —to (not necessary)
28 Page of song
32 —-vis
33 So be it!
35 Indian mulberry
36 Indian weight

9

PUZZLE 10

ACROSS

1 Bastinado
5 Pious (Ital.)
8 Band
9 Painter
13 Opposed to
14 Peanut
15 Beverage
16 Dish
17 Before
18 Godsends
20 Actress Scala
21 Illegalities
23 State (Fr.)
24 Biblical juniper tree
25 Struck
26 "John" in Moscow
27 Advised
28 Torme
29 Italian composer
30 Silkworm
31 Hawk parrot
32 Corpulent
35 Seek to date
37 Hairdo style
38 Goad
39 Whirl
40 German article
41 Soviet lake

DOWN

1 Conversation
2 First-rate
3 Completely dissimilar
4 Spire ornament
5 Idolaters
6 Golf clubs
7 Sioux
10 Not so!
11 Arranged in series
12 Handled
16 Frost offering
19 Foreshadow
21 — War (1853-1856)
22 Opposite
23 Exude
25 Iranian city
27 Thyroid problem
29 Greenland town
33 Region
34 Ringing
36 Singular
37 Macaw

PUZZLE 11

ACROSS

1 Nursery word
5 Booklets
11 Drooping
12 Fish type
13 Exist
14 Tooth substance
15 Pagoda ornament
16 Hairdo pad
17 Australian bird
18 Living
20 Child
21 Shade of blue
22 Shaft
23 Participate
25 Church council
26 Doggone it!
27 Late Aldo — of Italy
28 Swiss canton
29 Blake TV character
32 June beetle
33 Slower (mus.)
34 Concealed
35 Precept
37 Deer
38 Intertwine
39 "Picnic" playwright
40 Whirled
41 Czech river

DOWN

1 Medit. island
2 Foreign
3 Go around
4 Imitate
5 Compact
6 French annuity
7 Candlenut tree
8 Fail
9 Trill
10 Payed homage
16 Enthuse
19 Evangelist
22 Funeral mound
23 Feel horror
24 Leading role
25 Classify
27 Injured
29 Jenner or Cabot
30 Color
31 Snake
36 Cymbals
37 Hasten

PUZZLE 12

ACROSS

1 Starch source
5 Tower in India
10 Lummox
11 Stringent
12 Tropical ant
13 Actress Smith
14 Hooray!
15 Proper
16 Hissed sound
17 Church dignitary
19 Allegiance
20 Telegraph
21 Loving
22 Weight of Malay
23 Faction
24 Wearing shoes
25 Saint's symbol
26 Sesame
27 Gareth's love
30 Wood core
31 Make a choice
32 Chinese dynasty
33 Put back to work
35 Enumerate
36 Eaten away
37 Before (Lat.)
38 French novelist
39 Czech river

DOWN

1 Precipice
2 Sacrificial site
3 Shoot the works
4 Seraglio room
5 Free-for-all
6 — been had!
7 For a trifle
8 Revolting
9 Paused
11 Fry gently
15 Challenge
18 Song (Ger.)
21 Dossier
22 Illusion
23 Poverty
24 Looks
25 — up (promoted)
27 "Houseboat" star
28 Elegant style
29 Join
34 Crete mountain
35 New Guinea town

PUZZLE 13

ACROSS
1 "You — Me Love You..."
5 Extents
11 Metal
12 Dried corn food
13 Salamander
14 Primates
15 Girl's name
16 Metric measure
17 Conceit
18 Snake
20 Sailor
21 Maintain
22 Spanish lady
23 Boundary
24 "South Pacific" girl
25 Identical
26 Playwright Connelly
27 Threefold (pref.)
28 Diagram
31 Antiquated
32 Common suffix
33 Born (Fr.)
34 Doohickey
36 Nipa palm
37 Intertwine
38 Greek letter
39 More profound
40 Soviet lake

DOWN
1 Indian tower
2 Sports palace
3 In half
4 Inner (prefix)
5 Showed mercy
6 Scottish musician
7 Chemistry suffix
8 Concentrate
9 Opulent
10 Mrs. in Spain
16 Auk genus
19 Carry
22 Gossip
23 Nautical rope
24 Dilatory
25 Put away, as cargo
26 As a — of fact
28 Portion
29 Lariat
30 Asian country
35 Gender —
36 Arab garment

13

PUZZLE 14

ACROSS
1 Package
5 Fierce encounter
10 Encourage
11 Quiescent
13 Popular old song
15 Anger
16 "— live and breathe"
17 Tyke
18 Tracked down
20 Never (Ger.)
21 Half a score
22 Minus
23 Bowler's problem
26 Editor's mark
27 Mouth (sl.)
28 Color
29 Nonsense
30 Lecturer
33 Choose
34 Soul (Fr.)
35 Brown kiwi
37 Celebrate grandly (sl.)
40 Break the chains
41 Elysium
42 Lamprey catcher

43 Soccer great

DOWN
1 Indonesian island
2 Cancel a flight
3 Crowbar
4 French season
5 Singled out

6 Sensational
7 Ninny
8 Capt. Kirk portrayer
9 Abelard's love
12 Hate
14 Aspect
19 On tiptoes

22 Gangling
23 Walked
24 Intend
25 Type of gate
26 Spy in Canaan (Bib.)
28 —with (meddle)

30 Brownish gray
31 Eat away
32 Spur piece
36 Queen —'s lace
38 Indian cymbals
39 Ascot fabric

14

PUZZLE 15

ACROSS

1 Sunk fence
5 French cheese
10 Long time
11 Tiny aural appendage
13 Asian country (var.)
14 Cain was one
15 Bulgarian coin
16 Slapstick prop
17 Bombay title
18 Go wild
20 Food regimen
21 Riviera port
22 Let up
23 Don't — the boat
24 No — land
25 Abbe not a priest
26 Lower leg
27 German river
28 Punctually
31 Aunt, in Pamplona
32 Snoop
33 Lamprey
34 Indurate
36 Dross
37 Uncut
38 Italian river
39 Possessive pronoun
40 Belgian river

DOWN

1 Cheers
2 Concur
3 Perfect place
4 Use the "?"
5 Abreast
6 Congestive sound
7 A Gershwin
8 Blissful setting
9 Lady with a future
12 Hackneyed
16 Gregory —
19 Kitchen gadget
20 Gave out, as cards
23 Aglow
24 Goodly group
25 Myth. river
26 Trap
29 Civil War general
30 British composer
32 Persian fairy
35 German article
36 Tell

15

PUZZLE 16

ACROSS
1 Torture device
5 Before (prefix)
8 African lily
9 Certain cavalryman
13 Dreyfus' defender
14 Chant
15 Terminate
16 Farceur
17 Singular
18 Preordain
20 Grazing ground
21 Hue
22 Word of comparison
23 Susceptible
25 Diagram
26 In our circle
27 Any minute now
28 Fit — fiddle
29 "—, Amigos"
32 Man's nickname
33 Place
34 "— and Abner"
35 Paradisiacal
37 Attractive
38 "— Under the Elms"
39 Vegetable
40 Apiece
41 Gaze

DOWN
1 Demolished
2 Solitary
3 Places to store furs
4 N.Z. parrot
5 Yielding
6 Earshot
7 Inner (prefix)
10 Newman film
11 Becharm
12 Insect
16 — and dine
19 Prong
22 Pronoun of yore
23 — out (slowly got rid of)
24 Live at
25 — .45
27 Cup's complement
29 Shoot skyward
30 Outlandish
31 Besmirch
36 Sip
37 Steal (sl.)

16

PUZZLE 17

ACROSS

1 Wild hog
5 Poet
10 Spanish general
11 —Leh-mann
12 Rodgers-Hart musical
15 Sailor's assent
16 Caligula's greeting
17 Fit
18 Sault —Marie
19 Get an — effort (2 wds.)
20 Pin
23 Neophyte (var.)
24 Divulged
25 Single unit
26 Radar sound
27 Swing to and fro
28 Inlets (Sp.)
29 "Where —you?"
30 Sothern
31 Black cuckoo
32 Chinese weight
35 Infamous mobster

38 — fastener
39 Before (Lat.)
40 Actor, George —
41 Hitchcock's "— Window"

DOWN

1 Ali —
2 Palm leaf
3 Lane
4 Charlotte —
5 Lionel Bart musical
6 Cooked
7 Give —whirl
8 Raking with gunfire
9 Earthly
13 Surfeited
14 Actor, Woody —
18 Hitchcock's "The 39 —"
19 Expiate
20 Portu-guese navigator
21 Greasy state
22 Eternal or isosceles
25 Erich — Remar-que
27 Sen. Moynihan

31 Italian river
32 Whet-stone
33 Brazilian animal
34 Eur-opean river
36 Never Freud's nick-name
37 Spoil

17

PUZZLE 18

ACROSS

1 Wooden strip
5 Argot
9 —Falana
10 Like some plays
13 USSR inland sea
14 King of the Huns
15 Italian white wine
17 Sass
18 Attractive
20 Ooze
24 Sandarac tree
25 Walked
26 Greek island
27 Birds (Lat.)
28 Leant a hand
29 Reasoner and Mudd
32 Sumatran ape
33 Silver-tongued art
38 Without exception
40 Pa. city
41 Conveyed legally
42 Brazilian beast
43 "Second-Hand —"
44 Bring up the —

DOWN

1 Bridge term
2 Monk parrot
3 Sad cry
4 Bath powder
5 Tropical animal
6 Composer Bruckner
7 Mesh
8 Made-to-measure
11 Weather
12 Like some trousers
16 Over-whelmed
19 Indian garb
20 Punished
21 "—and Shirley"
22 Chilled Adam's ale
23 Army meal
26 Biblical town
30 Customs
31 Famed opera conductor
34 Sunder
35 French river
36 Donizetti opera
37 Fiscal —
39 Bridal response

PUZZLE 19

ACROSS

1 Bengal potentate
5 Irritated
11 Incite
12 Lounge
13 French illustrator
14 Warnings
15 Fuss
16 Frankie's second mate
17 Fitting
18 Did over
20 Swedish wine measure
21 Balanced
22 Pastry
23 Fleece
24 "John Brown's —"
25 Spanish belle
26 Nev. city
27 Portent
28 Actress, —Smith
31 June beetle
32 Rome's —Veneto
33 Monk
34 Brought out
36 Trench
37 Regal fabric
38 Greek river
39 Quake
40 Paradise

DOWN

1 MASH role
2 Dwelling
3 English writer
4 Had lunch
5 Cowardly
6 Loki's daughter
7 Imitate
8 English author
9 Sea inlet
10 Gobi is one
16 Arab seaport
19 Of birds
20 Expiate
23 Tea urn
24 Lugosi was one
25 Unas = suming
26 Combat specialist
29 Choleric
30 Pulpit topic
32 Negative
35 —Hunter
36 —Bush

19

PUZZLE 20

ACROSS

1 Colombian city
5 Cancel out
11 Moslem prayer call
12 —band
13 Musical style
15 Mining find
16 Add to lemon
17 Ceylon export
18 Measured
20 Business abbr.
21 Craggy spot
22 Lug
23 Lacerated
25 Camera feature
26 Uncommon
27 Storage container
28 Metric measure
29 Capital of New Mexico
33 Duct (biol.)
34 Anglo-Saxon king
35 English composer
36 Hep
39 Cargo derrick
40 Nasal sensation
41 Threw a party
42 Saucy

DOWN

1 Ricochet
2 Worship
3 Shoelace
4 Stationer's product
5 Famed reindeer
6 Called it off
7 Celtic deity
8 Love or anger, e.g.
9 Gifted persons
10 String about
14 He hit 755 home runs
19 To be (Fr.)
22 Pup—
23 Italian seaport
24 Iphigenia's brother
25 Ship
26 Plunder
27 Whacked
29 Screening device
30 Dwelling
31 Tend to prefer
32 Put forth effort
37 All—up
38 Alley—

PUZZLE 21

ACROSS

1 "— Loves Mambo"
5 Wash
10 Pulpit sign-off
11 Conceited one
13 French author
14 Holiday in Mexico
15 Metal
16 Sanskrit school
17 — and Magog
18 Additional
20 Anglo-Saxon king
21 King's title
22 Pleased look
23 White sauce
25 It needs dressing
26 Vicinity
27 St. Andrew's sport
28 "— Maria"
29 Clique
32 Vice
33 Spanish article
34 Author Levin
35 Shunned
37 European river
38 — tires
39 Sisters who sang
40 Taking no chances
41 Colored

DOWN

1 Gnocchi, e.g.
2 Violently
3 1941 Grant-Dunne movie
4 Ampersand
5 Preceding
6 Nimble
7 — the mark
8 1940 Grant-Russell movie
9 Iron Curtain country
12 Toward the finish
16 Lacerated
19 Gesture silently
22 Outburst
23 Follow-up drink
24 Rebirth
25 Barflies
27 Large
29 Manifest
30 Byzantine empress
31 Otate
36 German article
37 Mature

21

PUZZLE 22

ACROSS

1 Bird coop
5 Ball of yarn
9 Rumanian city
10 Of certain birds
13 Spanish money
14 Curtain raiser
15 "Brother —" (1938 film)
16 "The Wayward —"
17 Judaism convert
18 Fatty
20 Greek letter
21 Shade of green
22 Yemen seaport
23 Sire
25 Fix
26 At loose —
27 Bombay attire
28 Greek deity
29 Imperfect ones
32 Moroccan mtn. range
33 "— pro nobis"
34 Stannum
35 Glacial epoch
37 "That's a —!"
38 Ex-Boston soccer team
39 Therefore
40 Biblical weed
41 Watched

DOWN

1 Director Frank
2 Nymph
3 Losing
4 Old Tokyo
5 Lindsay —
6 Memory blank
7 French season
8 Representation of Nike
11 Squirrel monkey
12 Wandering
16 Quit the party
19 Filled goodies
22 English river
23 Grin and —
24 Beguile
25 Malayan VIP
27 Tranquil
29 Airman's O.K.
30 Coloration
31 Hair covering
36 Candlenut tree
37 Born

PUZZLE 23

ACROSS

1 Chew the fat
5 Weight shedder
11 Solitary
12 "When —..." (advice to a tourist)
13 Before (Lat.)
14 Grave of most U-boats
15 Cheer
16 Mongrel
17 Do badly
18 Spiritual adherent
20 Chemical suffix
21 Location
22 Love deity
23 European river
25 Some Lapps
26 Touch upon
27 Leading man's role
28 Malay gibbon
29 Of Toledo
32 Entirely
33 Fiery
34 Tijuana uncle
35 Worked hard
37 Payment
38 Imbue
39 Talented
40 Looked like
41 College in Oregon

DOWN

1 Bow in films
2 Chinese province
3 1942 Bette Davis film
4 Born (Fr.)
5 Stop using
6 Sluggish
7 Memorable days
8 1942 Jack Benny film
9 Essayist-poet
10 Reparation
16 Quote
19 Candy
22 Ireland
23 Deli items
24 Ear shell
25 Hat fabric
27 Masked
29 Not those
30 Church path
31 Illustrious
36 "— and Abner"
37 Detroit export

PUZZLE 24

ACROSS
1 French priest
5 French painter
11 Ringlet
12 Stimulate
13 Prune
14 Ohio city
15 Sea eagle
16 Wee sibling
17 Arena cry
18 Darn it!
20 Cigaret (Brit. sl.)
21 Narrative
22 Observe
23 Purpose
25 Worked the earth
26 Lacerated
27 Penalize
28 United
29 Card game
32 Seraglio room
33 Success
34 Congregate
35 Of the mails
37 Fluff
38 Woman's name
39 Vase handle
40 Like some fenders
41 German river

DOWN
1 Played a part
2 Mexican donkey
3 Convince
4 Tree
5 Wisconsin city
6 Expunge
7 "Sine qua —"
8 Frantic
9 Quarantine
10 Backed out
16 Unique
19 Stare
22 Columbus' ship
23 Condescended
24 Express sympathy
25 — julep
27 Flunked
29 Pursuit
30 On edge
31 Rose essence
36 — for tat
37 New Guinea town

PUZZLE 25

ACROSS
1 Float
5 Capacity
10 European capital
11 So what?
13 Pardon me!
14 Inculcate
15 Vast area
16 Likely
17 Crisscross
18 Diamond feat
20 Explosive letters
21 At no time (poet.)
22 Gaming cubes
23 Not quite right
25 Fiasco cause
26 Monthly expense
27 Bell
28 Blvd.
29 Rob on TV
32 Why not?
33 Black substance
34 Palm leaf
35 Webfooter State
37 Emperor
38 Was getting there
39 Network
40 Business
41 French river

DOWN
1 Excoriate
2 Jacob's son
3 Notion (sl.)
4 Jones or Seaver
5 Unseen marksman
6 Bridge (Fr.)
7 Nickname of 1936
8 Checking attendance (sl.)
9 Gist
12 Could be Irish
16 Downwind side
19 Nuisance
22 Ceylonese vessel
23 Drawing item
24 Young hare
25 Dutch S. African
27 Rio —
30 Fill with joy
31 Less common
33 Kicked along
36 Irish "sweet heart"
37 Go at it

25

PUZZLE 26

ACROSS

1 Nucleus
5 Abstinent
10 Greek letter
12 Track down
13 Not in the big time
15 Mel of baseball
16 Rivulet
17 Taunt
18 — and order
21 Pulley
24 Just dandy
25 Grand schemes
27 Different
28 Biblical mountain
29 Trouble
30 Men only
31 Numerical suffix
32 N.M. Indian
35 Inferior
39 Greek mtn.
40 Bald —
41 "— Parisienne"
42 Judge to be

DOWN

1 Perry who's not Mason
2 Exclude
3 Pay to use
4 Big "I"
5 Stone marker
6 By mouth
7 Capture
8 Medieval shield
9 Caddoan Indian
11 Make one's mark
14 Like modern women
17 Cimino's "Heaven's —"
18 Deceiver
19 — Christie
20 Occident
21 Pintail duck
22 Saintly symbol
23 To be (Lat.)
24 "It's a grand old —..."
26 Strut
30 Apprehend
31 Binge
32 Learned one
33 Eyot
34 Ancient gold alloy
35 Droop
36 Greek letter
37 "The Windy City"
38 Stripling

PUZZLE 27

ACROSS

1 Starting point
5 Actor Aykroyd
8 Among
9 S.C. river
13 Famous engraver
14 TV newsman
15 Persian rose
16 —Bertha
17 Ex-Boston Bruin
18 Eroding
20 Lode's yield
21 Regarding
22 Agent (suff.)
23 More rational
25 Richard of car racing
26 Gaelic
27 Speed of sound
28 Slower (mus.)
29 "—Gold" (1936 film)
32 Compass reading
33 Three, to Lisi
34 Diamond wood
35 Less sloppy
37 Moon (Fr)
38 Turkish city
39 Seaweed
40 Spanish for king
41 Extorted money from

DOWN

1 Law officer's symbol
2 It's love to Belmondo
3 Cut of beef
4 Dutch city
5 Deduce
6 Maxim
7 Basketball tourney (abbr.)
10 Tell tall tales
11 Harness ring
12 Planetarium
16 Wind force
19 Old dagger
22 Religious body
23 Woman's name
24 Gone on high
25 Head
27 Arthur or Don
29 Cubic meter
30 Scope
31 Stand one in good —
36 Sailor
37 Study room

PUZZLE 28

ACROSS

1 Manhandle
5 Populace
9 Canyon mouth
10 Archie's TV mate
12 Asian desert
13 Spoiled
15 Marsh plant
16 Ship's diary
17 Before
18 Expurgate
20 Bard's adverb
21 Murderous
22 Coal —
23 Deep-felt
25 "Waiting for —"
27 Palance film
28 Mexican Indian
29 Jordanian mountain
30 Dependents
33 "— Tu?"
34 — Van Winkle
35 Reagan seldom wears one
36 Gloomy
38 To be (Fr.)
39 Schedule
40 Cruel
41 Town in Mass.
42 Shoe —

DOWN

1 Blackstone's forte
2 Overhead
3 Revolutionary
4 Chou En—
5 Recollection
6 Old saying
7 Knightly title
8 Rough, tough guy
11 At this place
14 Irish county
16 Decoy
19 Lush
23 Hurts
24 Refrain
25 — year
26 Go wrong
28 Black eye
30 Greek island
31 American painter
32 Stone marker
37 Secular
38 Salamander

PUZZLE 29

ACROSS

1 City in Iraq
6 Garbage
11 Desire
12 Vietnam capital
13 African river
15 Hockey great
16 Go wrong
17 Indian weight
18 Russian measure
20 Deny
23 Dog in "Beetle Bailey"
26 Poet
27 Baptism and others
28 African beast
29 Attacks
30 Strength
32 Ninny
34 By way of
35 Hitchcock as a boy?
38 Stephen Foster song
41 Old German dollar
42 Humming sound
43 Untalented
44 Apprehend

DOWN

1 Action (Sp.)
2 African gazelle
3 Assert
4 Civil War soldier
5 Minimally
6 Thither
7 Functioned
8 Liqueur
9 Unique
10 Here (Ger.)
14 Compulsion
18 — B. Anthony
19 Boisterous
20 Nonsense
21 Taro root
22 Where shoppers go to blazes?
24 Holiday in 12 Across
25 Ladd film
27 Word ending a letter
29 French cheese
31 Tennis star
32 — spumante
33 — song (last work)
35 Earl of —
36 Camera part
37 Manumit
39 Catnip
40 Anger

29

PUZZLE 30

ACROSS

1 Golf club
5 Belt
9 Famed "Melancholy" one
10 Walter — Disney
12 Chicago Fair danceuse
15 Taro root
16 Ventilate
17 Patriotic group
18 Brace
20 Before
21 Work unit
22 Minus
23 Was solicitous
26 Helping hands
27 Jewish month
28 Sweetie pie
29 Poppycock!
30 Brazilian river
33 Table scrap
34 Hill dweller
35 Drummer Blakey
37 12 Across was one

40 Am. Rev. patriot
41 Italian river
42 Whirl
43 Globule

DOWN

1 Not working
2 Military exploits
3 Vic — torious
4 NBA N.J. member
5 Understanding
6 Ever vigilant
7 Man's nickname
8 Bumpkin
11 Meager
13 Nixon cabinet member
14 Ringlet

19 Unfriendly look
22 Soprano Pagliughi
23 Medit. bean
24 Worshiped
25 Deadly biter
26 Blood vessel
28 Famed composer

30 "Miracle on 34th St." star
31 Mother-of-pearl
32 Sports setting
36 Trampled
38 New Guinea town
39 Collar

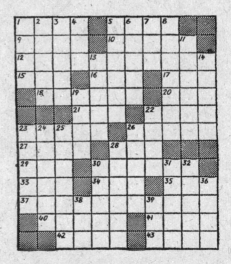

30

PUZZLE 31

ACROSS
1 Price mark
6 Famous Indian's horse
11 Popeye's girlfriend
12 Outmoded
13 Classic dessert
15 "My — and Only"
16 Half a tenner
17 Elec. unit
19 Snare
22 Carefree
25 Of aircraft
26 Cheesy dish
28 On
29 Moses of the NBA
30 Long for
31 Moon feature
32 Rested
33 Wreath
36 Breakfast treat
41 Adversary
42 Originate
43 Maxim
44 Sacred symbol

DOWN
1 Timber wolf
2 Hunting dog
3 Messenger's need
4 Night before
5 Guided
6 Rent
7 Sonny Corleone portrayer
8 CIA forerunner
9 Welsh river
10 Oolong
14 Result
17 Insect
18 Rowan tree
19 Biblical mount
20 Hibernia
21 Carry
22 Absent
23 Head (Fr.)
24 N.C. college
25 Competent
27 Swiss river
31 Twin crystal
32 Obstacle
33 Cafe au —
34 Abstract being
35 Detail
36 Monk's title
37 Make free from
38 Wagnerian heroine
39 Make lace
40 Gold (Sp.)

31

PUZZLE 32

ACROSS

1 Military setting
5 Type of brick
10 Asian river
11 Debonair
13 Optimistic
14 Mobster's threat
15 Yale student
16 On strike
17 Meadow
18 Stage settings
20 Liquid measure
21 Senior (Fr.)
22 Undies trim
23 Thousand, in Tours
25 Took a gamble
26 Formerly
27 "On Golden —"
28 Annealing oven
29 Tex or son John
32 Generation
33 Russian river
34 Altar in the heavens
35 Agitate
37 Ski lift
38 Diatribe
39 Different
40 Showy flower
41 Ruminant

DOWN

1 Showed an interest
2 Soap plant
3 Parlor game
4 Snoop
5 Excite
6 Dash
7 Turkish weight
8 Pool parlor fixture
9 Perfume
12 In anger
16 French river
19 Ship
20 Secret informant
23 Maltreat
24 Sluggishness
25 "— What Comes Natur'lly"
27 Correct
30 Expunge
31 Less usual
33 One kind of ranch
36 Traitor
37 Work with fodder

PUZZLE 33

ACROSS

1 Attenuated
5 Solo melody
9 Integrity
11 Ballroom dance
13 Between (Fr.)
14 Incompetent
15 Alkali
16 Bon —
18 "Who am — argue?"
19 Junkyard, for one
21 Actress Fabray, to some
22 Prima donna
23 Lavish party
24 Absconded with
26 Certain prisoner
27 Summons
28 Prong
29 Alderman (abbr.)
30 Any ship's boat
33 Malay gibbon
34 Tatter
35 Weight unit
36 Island off Venezuela
38 "—Frome"
40 Ice-coated
41 Della of song
42 Regarding
43 Greek river

DOWN

1 "Is That All —Is?"
2 Sweetie pie
3 Down-hearted
4 And not
5 Deep-felt
6 Nancy's mate
7 Healthy
8 Arouse
10 Eradicate
12 Penitent one
17 "...man —mouse?"
20 Doorway feature
23 Helsinki native
24 Math term
25 Mercury's sandals
26 Tarry
28 Aunt (Sp.)
30 Spanish museum
31 Shore
32 Nine (comb. form)
37 Wager
39 "— for Two"

PUZZLE 34

ACROSS

1 The two
5 Initiate
10 Son of Jacob
12 Kind
   of beer
13 Gawk
14 Playing
   marble
15 Smite
16 Dismiss
   (sl.)
18 Author
   Levin
19 Acquiesce
21 Late Cole
22 Pup —
23 Frilly
24 Have a talk
25 Hundred
   (Fr.)
26 "Silkwood"
   co-star
27 "On Golden
   —"
28 Holbrook
29 Fatal
31 Silkworm
32 Bridal
   response
33 "I — Ideas"
   (1951 song)
35 Famous
   violinist
37 So. Amer.
   cattle
39 Fishing
   net
40 Hercules'
   horse
41 Chemical
   compound
42 Sicilian
   city

DOWN

1 Thwack
2 Rome's
   old port
3 I've
   had it!
4 Not him
5 Distort
   in writing
6 Tyke's
   game
7 Repeatedly
8 Take back
9 Pact
11 New
17 Emmet
20 Burn
23 Made a
   loan
24 Princess
   Di's mate
25 Cigar style
26 Grated
   or cream
27 Seed vessel
29 Pay-dirt
   finder
30 Pretend
34 River
   in Kenya
36 Chem-
   istry
   suffix
38 Choler

PUZZLE 35

ACROSS

1 Cook
5 Jazz fan
8 Songstress O'Day
10 Give a speech
13 Part of a stair
14 God, the creator
15 Alan Ladd film
16 Link
18 Go wrong
19 Least unkempt
21 Mouths (Lat.)
22 Standard
23 Presently
24 Songstress Helen
26 Bergen's Mortimer
27 TV award
28 Country (Span.)
29 Farrow
30 Corpulent
33 Sort
34 Inlet (Sp.)
35 Late Onassis
36 Basso Cesare
38 Craze
40 Fry gently
41 So. Amer. Indian
42 Average
43 Actress Daly

DOWN

1 Nobleman
2 Liqueur flavoring
3 Settle a tiff
4 Hot time in Paris
5 Celestial body
6 Macaw
7 Fascinate, as a blind date
9 Highway branch
11 Panic
12 Task
17 Doctrine
20 West Indies bird
23 Indigo plant
24 Negligent
25 Iago's wife
26 Deli item
28 Canadian province (abbr.)
30 More ironic
31 Of a Great Lake
32 Actress Keaton
37 School group
39 Formic acid source

35

PUZZLE 36

ACROSS

1 Bellow
5 "For — the Bell Tolls"
9 Different
10 Afghan city
12 Location
13 Ankara inn
15 Beyond help
17 Vets' group from 1866
18 Snuggery
19 — standstill
20 Exertion
24 Dry
25 English river
26 White sauce
27 Ukraine legis-lature
28 Calorie counter
29 Berlin outcry
30 Floor covering
31 Andress film
32 Electra's brother
37 Fall or spring
39 Ace in the —
40 Originate
41 Opera highlight
42 Asian weight
43 Substance

DOWN

1 Remainder
2 Potpourri
3 Regarding
4 Old-time dance
5 Blanch
6 Macho guys
7 Mouths (anat.)
8 British princess
11 British tradition
14 Stock exchange member
16 Mine entrance
20 Paste
21 Windpipe
22 Valentine symbol
23 Collection of facts
24 "All the Things You —"
26 Quote
28 Type of grass
30 Big game
33 Fake
34 Lacerated
35 Lamb's pen name
36 — belt
38 Keresan Indian

PUZZLE 37

ACROSS
1 Deceit
5 Confine
9 Mister (Ger.)
10 Ryan or Tatum
12 Eng. composer
13 Cookery staple
15 Probable winner
17 A Gabor
18 Single
19 Marsh
20 Official seal
24 "Marriage Feast" site
25 Son of Jacob
26 Snake
27 Gush out
28 Restore to health
29 — in the sky
30 Guzzler
31 Go wrong
32 Reverential
37 Contravene
39 Chilling glance
40 Poe's sleuth
41 Ital. wine center
42 Cantrell of song
43 Orson —

DOWN
1 Dance step
2 Intrepid one
3 Italian river
4 Alan Young's old TV show
5 Convincing
6 Explorer Juan de —
7 Over (poet.)
8 Bob Hope film
11 Perked up
14 Shade of yellow
16 Dutch S. African
20 Wyoming city
21 Had ambitions
22 Merry
23 Conform
24 English river
26 Network (anat.)
28 Ivanhoe's beloved
30 Fine fabric
33 Pitcher's plate
34 Bacteriologist's wire
35 Half (Ital.)
36 Ireland
38 —tree (cornered)

37

PUZZLE 38

ACROSS

1 Corday's victim
6 Musical notes
10 Light sarcasm
11 Maturing
13 Marcello of films
15 TV Tarzan
16 Islet
17 Persian rose
18 Alone
19 Ancient days
20 Mulelike animal
22 Heraldic wreath
23 Terry Southern novel
24 Grilled
25 Commedia dell'—
26 Languished
27 Dutch city
28 Sharpen
29 Indian weight
30 Palm leaf
31 Decay
34 "The Rose Tattoo" star
37 Can. town official
38 Spear
39 Doe or roe
40 Register

DOWN

1 Roman farce
2 Russian lake
3 Optimistic
4 Picnic "gate-crasher"
5 Despotism
6 Church-going masses
7 Moslem ruler
8 The "Undie World," in catalogs
9 Invali-dated
12 "...bird in a — cage"
14 Unctuous
18 Wavy (her.)
20 Callous
21 P.O.W.
22 French river
23 Comedian or salad
24 Be sly
26 Actress Negri
28 Classical poet
31 Rave
32 Formerly
33 Pinafore
35 Caligula's greeting
36 Variant of Anne

38

PUZZLE 39

ACROSS

1 Nursemaid of the Orient
5 Gather
10 Feather
11 Penitent thief
13 Sandarac tree
14 At reduced prices
15 Disclose
17 Ignited
18 Pronoun
19 Hire
20 Hair covering
23 Resiliency
24 Flower
25 Subsequently
26 Vase handle
27 Actor Philip
28 Colorado Indian
29 Saint (Sp.)
30 Caesar
31 Oklahoma city
36 Isolate
38 Hunting dog
39 Concoct
40 Swiss herdsman
41 One with Hansen's disease
42 Bye, British style

DOWN

1 Grandparental
2 Adele of the late show
3 Fruit
4 Trumpeter —Alpert
5 Wellbeloved
6 Clementine's father
7 Simpleton
8 Quick drink
9 Emphasis
12 Parlor piece
16 Tar's greeting
20 Guardsman
21 Sudden decline (sl.)
22 "— Clear Day"
23 Shooting match (Fr.)
24 Hesitated
25 Novelist George—
27 One's lifework
29 Volcano mud
32 Mizzen
33 Olive genus
34 Rave
35 Sicilian city
37 Drink

39

PUZZLE 40

ACROSS

1 Painted bunting
5 French clerics
10 Adored one
11 Threatening phrase
12 Hood
13 Trim of figure
14 Miner's gain
15 Smote
16 Off one's —
17 Of this earth
19 Burmese knife
20 Passenger
21 Horse
22 Before-mentioned
23 Strong-flavored
24 Cut of beef
25 Aida's "—Scene"
26 With no exception
27 Mound of boulders
30 Grk. and Heb. letter
31 Eddie Fisher's "—Time"
32 Game marble
33 Wandering
35 Location
36 Ornamental work
37 Gray with age
38 Savory
39 "My One and—"

DOWN

1 Lace ornament
2 Venerate
3 Outages
4 Building wing
5 Mountain ridge
6 Put up cash
7 Lawyer John Dean's book
8 Arm of the sea
9 Do a slow burn
11 Air a view
15 Cattle group
18 Joan Crawford film
21 Papa's love
22 Sun rooms
23 Murderous
24 Dormant
25 He said "Kemo Sabe"
27 Virile
28 Of birth
29 Old-time closet
34 Hgt.
35 Japanese measure

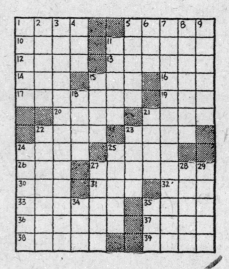

40

PUZZLE 41

ACROSS

1 Of the cheek
6 Impudence (sl.)
11 Mountain ridge
12 Spear
13 Certain Canadian
15 Chemical suffix
16 Weight
17 Wing (Lat.)
18 By maiden name
19 Arena cheer
20 Countdown word
21 Cunning
22 Hundred (Fr.)
23 Heal
25 Container
26 Having left us
27 Secular
28 "For Me — My Gal"
29 English river
30 Rest
33 Between Can. and Mex.
34 Lode's product
35 Danish money

36 What to do to meet 13 across
39 Student (Fr.)
40 Address the convention
41 Kind of car
42 Wearied

DOWN

1 Masssenet opera
2 Came about

3 Embankment
4 "I'm — loss for words"
5 Bring back
6 Biological "ditto"
7 Nogoodik
8 Eastern church members
9 Type of triangle

10 Inhabit
14 Corral youngster
21 "Where — the snows..."
22 Islet
23 TV set style
24 Like many spinsters?
25 Harris-Redgrave film

26 Measures
27 Christie film role
29 Myron of comedy
30 As of today
31 Angry
32 Strained
37 Eggs
38 Bela's son

PUZZLE 42

ACROSS

1 Estimate
5 Saw
10 Exclude
11 Failing in mind
13 Fruit type
14 Whine
15 Before
16 Knotts or Adams
17 Wagnerian role
18 Clerical residence
20 Insurrectionist Turner
21 Measure
22 Lavish affair
23 Helicopter part
25 Intimated
26 Not odd
27 Unmoved
28 Ending for rub
29 Goblet
32 Where —thou?
33 On a winning streak
34 Way off
35 One "in stitches"?
37 —apparent
38 Site of Mark Twain's grave

39 To be (Fr.)
40 Flat
41 Painter, Grant —

DOWN

1 Tied, as a calf
2 Love, in Livorno
3 Repeatedly
4 Monsieur's summer
5 Classify
6 Bulldog Drummond's butler
7 Cuckoo
8 Reinvigorate
9 Set on high

12 Overjoyed
16 Forest creature
19 Showy sign
22 —'s errand
23 Partial refund
24 Generally
25 —of arms

27 Certain societies
29 Bit of work
30 "Maltese Falcon" character
31 Made a mistake
36 Ullmann
37 Cut down

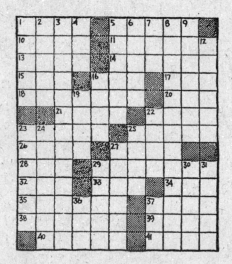

PUZZLE 43

ACROSS

1 Julia Ward —
5 Simpleton
8 Turkish city
10 Treaty
12 Troy name
13 American soprano
15 Clumsy craft
16 Needlefish
18 Suit size (abbr.)
19 Eyot
21 Malay gibbon
22 Converge
24 Literary Adam
25 Hiss' first, Horatio's last
26 It's on the cover
27 Corded fabric
28 Moved around
29 M.G.M. name
30 Her name means "beautiful"
31 Faucet
32 Draper's measure
33 Dress up
36 Harsh
38 Chemical compound
40 "— go Bragh"
41 Della of song
42 Influence
43 Three, in cards

DOWN

1 How droll!
2 European river
3 Notice of dismissal
4 Chemistry suffix
5 Separated
6 Dooley Wilson role
7 Hester's "A"
9 Fisherman
11 Foot lever
14 Concurred
17 Chalice veil
20 "— lively!"
22 "Forty —"
23 Ennoble
24 Beak or poster
26 Steering device
28 Blanc or Ferrer
30 Late Waukegan comic
34 Bacteriologist's wire
35 Zane —
37 Inlet
39 Group

43

PUZZLE 44

ACROSS

1 Hazard
5 Reached
10 Showy flower
12 Dodge
13 Lasso
14 "— of Endearment"
15 Sea eagle
16 By way of
18 Basketball tourney (abbr.)
19 True Americans
21 Grass variety
22 Store event
23 Insect
24 One kind of agent
26 American clergyman
27 Eye part
28 German author
29 This (Sp.)
30 Fasten
33 P.I. people
34 Favorite
35 Mauna —
36 Biblical mountain
38 Antelope
40 Happening

41 Funeral music
42 Moratorium
43 Role for Freeman Gosden

DOWN

1 Less common
2 French river
3 Act as guard
4 Egyptian weight unit
5 "— move on!"
6 Bullring cheer
7 Call the fire fighters
8 Naval V.I.P.
9 Leaving a valid will
11 Disentangles
17 Suffix
20 Billiard shot
21 Emissary
24 Gratified
25 Unruly
26 Caressed

28 West
31 River that Stanley explored
32 Hell
34 Mercy
37 Collection
39 — Fail (crowning stone)

44

PUZZLE 45

ACROSS

1 Niblick or putter, e.g.
5 Beach
11 Mature
12 Mideast peninsula
13 Among
14 Scottish lake
15 Forbid
16 Moisture
17 Written letter
18 Pagoda ornament
20 Before
22 Comic Myron
24 Untied
27 Beyond
28 — pricing
29 Unspoken
31 Metric unit
32 Peggy of song
33 Bandleader Brown
34 Fuss
36 Actor Scheider
38 Tricked
41 Praised
43 Father (Fr.)
44 Write
45 Picnic spoiler
46 Rot
47 Whirlpool

DOWN

1 Sourpuss
2 Ohio city
3 In a reverie
4 Foundation
5 Shopper stopper
6 Mason's implement
7 Crash against
8 Too deep for
9 Number of Muses
10 Florida county
16 Cozy room
19 Unearthly
21 Course
22 Barracks item
23 Eggs
25 Gielgud's title
26 Summer (Fr.)
30 Cylindrical
31 Foxy
34 Arabic letter
35 Hamlet was one
37 European river
39 Barren
40 Gainsay
42 Morse Code sound
43 Prior to (pref.)

45

PUZZLE 46

ACROSS

1 Facts
5 Booklet
10 German lancer
11 TV anchorman
13 Hammer of fiction
14 Cling
15 Golf score
16 Black cuckoo
17 Dernier —
18 Pacino film
20 Jayhawk State (abbr.)
21 Ireland
22 Lab animals
23 Breeding places
25 Ship
26 Potpourri
27 Soft drink
28 Little Edgar
29 Jerry who had Hope
32 Years lived
33 Indian mulberry
34 De Luise
35 Role for Mike Connors
37 Eur. fruit tree
38 Curtain call
39 Stratagem
40 Purport
41 Road (Lat.)

DOWN

1 French author
2 Marble of tennis
3 Dwell in
4 Chemistry suffix
5 Hypnotic state
6 Drive-time medium
7 Belgian town
8 Have a short stay
9 Raised level
12 Fritz or Carl
16 Tunes
19 Flax
22 Venus's island
23 "— Jive" (1940's song)
24 Tasteful
25 Droop
27 Cajoler
29 Egyptian city
30 Scandinavian
31 "Forever —"
36 Sine qua —
37 — Lanka

46

PUZZLE 47

ACROSS

1 Former name of 33 Across
5 Trident, e.g.
10 Take a cab
11 Thornton or Gene
13 Arabian sultanate
14 Smitten by Cupid
15 Fraternity —
16 Likely
17 Opp. to Dem.
18 Kitchen or card —
20 Boundary
21 Color for a flying Baron
22 Swedish girl's name
23 Oregon city
26 Great with lox
27 Old oath
28 Beach hue
29 Italian river
30 Legislate
33 Ring name
34 Bishop's seat
35 Jordanian mountain
37 Tried out
39 Skid row character
40 Jewish ascetic
41 Court minutes
42 American jockey
43 Thug

DOWN

1 Harvest
2 Confine
3 Turkish city
4 Craving
5 Stole (sl.)
6 Liquid measure
7 Building section
8 Worshipful
9 Vendetta
12 Rescind
16 Turkish flag
19 Dutch city
20 Climbing vine
23 Part of "S.P.Q.R."
24 Eternal
25 City in Thessaly
26 Curse
28 Another spelling of "touch down"
31 A Marx man
32 Fictional Indian
34 Dispatch
36 Horse
38 Half a score
39 Humorist

47

PUZZLE 48

ACROSS

1 Son of Jacob
6 Long Island resort town
11 Chevy —
12 Not a soul
13 Raged
14 Creator of Nero Wolfe
15 Before
16 Farming tool
18 Sumatran ape
19 Turn aside
21 Douglas —
22 Lacerate
23 Role for Connery
24 Muslim official
25 Tennis name
26 Summon
27 Cat cry
28 Lubricate
29 Hundred-weight (Brit.)
31 Pamplona's "gold"
32 Brown kiwi
33 L.A. football pro
35 Embankment

37 Mountain —
39 Sluggish
40 Join in
41 Lead-tin alloy
42 Sleeper's sound

DOWN

1 Farmer's holding
2 Pottery fragment

3 Surpass
4 Direction (abbr.)
5 Verdon musical
6 Map feature
7 Drunkard
8 Expect
9 Habi-tuating

10 Explosive device
17 Hockey great
20 Facial garment
23 Kick
24 From Egypt's capital
25 Indian city

26 Calm down
27 Farmer of India
29 Greek island
30 Beer variety
34 Bare
36 Sea eagle
38 Hostelry

48

PUZZLE 49

ACROSS

1 Redshank
5 —Munson
8 Mad king
9 Poem
13 Formerly
14 Set in harmony
15 Burmese knife
16 Consumed
17 Greek letter
18 Drugged
20 Author Deighton
21 Pursued
23 "Gentle on My —"
24 Felled
25 Card game
26 Eng. composer
27 Irish—
28 Reine's husband
29 Wasteland
30 Amongst
31 Vaudeville feature
32 Go wrong
35 Isolate
37 On water
38 Smelled like a stogie
39 Dip into
40 Wrath
41 Price paid

DOWN

1 Oaf
2 "Victory" heroine
3 1939 Cagney-Raft film
4 Before
5 Gave a speech
6 Illustrious
7 Tiny tunneler

10 1946 Peck film
11 Harmony between nations
12 Hero's beloved
16 Mocked
19 O.T. book

21 Lovable one
22 Intrepid one
23 N.Y.C. street
25 Substance
27 Quit the group

29 Old Ger. coin
33 Torn apart
34 Libertine
36 Go schus-sing
37 Dean Martin film

PUZZLE 50

ACROSS
1 Location
5 Tempo
9 Cowardly Lion
10 Patriotic song
13 S-shaped
14 Literary extracts
15 Selleck
16 June bug
17 "Mr. Tambourine—"
18 Think
20 Wood sorrel
21 Ghosts
23 N.Y.C. street
24 On edge
25 Bequest recipient
26 Pa. city
27 Live in
28 Beast of burden
29 Monthly costs
30 Ugly throng
31 A Carter
32 Female parent
35 Twine around
37 Douglas novel, with "The"
38 Besmeared
39 Pitcher
40 Unearthly
41 Before (Lat.)

DOWN
1 Animal's track
2 Crossword villain
3 Preminger film
4 —long
5 Roger and Francis
6 Finnish lake
7 Siamese coin
8 Steinbeck novel
11 Put into law
12 Sea cow
16 Dam
19 Affectation
21 Lost their cool
22 Role one assumes
23 Greatest
25 Refuse
27 Correct
29 Snake
33 Encourage
34 Mother (Fr.)
36 Called "Honest"
37 Turmeric

PUZZLE 51

ACROSS

1 Oliver Hardy's nickname
5 Topknot
10 Arab seaport
11 ——day Saint
13 French author
14 Breathe in
15 Heckler's "missile"
16 Table piece
17 ——Aviv
18 Ocean route
20 Epoch
21 Church season
22 Photocopy
23 Leafy food
25 German city
26 Irish island group
27 Major——
28 Anais——
29 Down to business
32 Sleuth (sl.)
33 Pugilist, Lee——
34 "——bono publico"
35 Verdi opera
37 Bridle part
38 One kind of jacket
39 Algerian city
40 Out of the way
41 Pallid

DOWN

1 Some are stolen
2 Aphorism
3 Colonial British soldiers
4 Purpose
5 Patron
6 Roam
7 Numerical suffix
8 Certain police officers
9 Aircraft navigation system
12 Pertain
16 Debark
19 Incline
22 Truck
23 Brazilian seaport
24 Operatic song
25 Israeli dance
27 Reduce in rank
29 Cubic in shape
30 ——Heep
31 Bono without Cher
36 Chou En——
37 Brown kiwi

PUZZLE 52

ACROSS

1 Raison d'
—
5 Precepts
9 Top roles
11 Different
13 Wall
bracket
14 Gaze
15 Noah (Bib.)
16 Mamie's
husband
18 Nervous
twitch
19 Medicine
dispenser
21 Held a
session
22 Want
23 His name
is a
palindrome
24 Merriment
26 Anesthetic
27 Coarse file
28 French
cheese
29 Tree
30 G.I. on
parade
33 Finn
seaport
34 Harem
room
35 Rubber
tree
36 Attack
38 Bellini
opera

40 Eat away
41 Weary
42 Three,
in cards
43 Ancient
harp

DOWN

1 Antelope
2 Jon Vickers
is one
3 Be in a
hurry (sl.)
4 Old Tokyo
5 One
defeated
6 Lawyer
(abbr.)
7 Slow down!
8 Set in
series
10 Hidden
marksman
12 Clergyman
17 Sheep
tick
20 Bo —
23 Of the
ear
24 Fold
25 Old-
time
weapon
26 Wandering

28 "Big —
John"
30 Folding
—
31 — J. Fudd
32 English
novelist
37 "— to
Billy Joe"
39 Iran's
"capital"

PUZZLE 53

ACROSS
1 Pump
5 Battle memento
9 Zero —
10 Cards of fortune
12 Greek river
13 Turkish city
15 "Zip-a-Dee-Doo—"
16 Favoring
17 Rubicund
18 Pupil (Fr.)
20 Thrash
21 Elf
23 Squirrel monkey
24 Susceptible
25 Fraud
26 Change the decor
27 Pull back
28 Powdered lava
29 Actress Berger
30 Suffix for meteor
31 Success
32 Malay gibbon
35 TV's Lear
37 Spanish painter
38 Not a body
39 Hebrides island
40 Its flesh is venison
41 Presently

DOWN
1 Food fish
2 Israeli dance
3 Exaggerate
4 Time period
5 Famish
6 Outrigger
7 B.C. boat
8 Bellow
11 Dealt with
14 Extol
16 Baseball's Rose
19 Type-setting machine (colloq.)
21 Wrench
22 "Music Man" actor
23 Savoir-faire
25 Slit in a garment
27 Fritz or Rob
29 Alan Ladd film
33 Firenze's river
34 Horse
36 A Stooge
37 Farrow

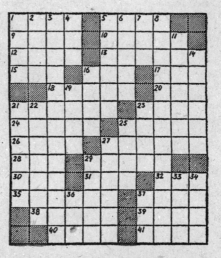

PUZZLE 54

ACROSS

1 "The —
   Tattoo"
5 Thwacked
11 Athirst
12 Fly
13 Boundary
   line
14 Afr.
   wildcat
15 Golf
   instructor
16 Rhyme-
   ster's
   adverb
17 Summer
   (Fr.)
18 Act the
   fishwife
20 Cambric
   or iced
22 Bishop's
   hat
24 Measure
   poetry
27 Different
28 Accum-
   ulate
29 Adolescent
30 Heavenly
   sight
31 Obese
33 Golf score
34 Beverage
36 Success
38 Snuggery
41 Loving
43 Extinct
   bird
44 Revenue

45 Pitcher
46 Gazed
47 A Bronte
   DOWN
1 Inclined
   way
2 Done with
3 Be neutral
4 Dutch city
5 Foundation

6 Fend off
7 Knightly
   title
8 Be deflated
9 Coup d'
   —
10 Cross out
16 Czech river
19 Boxing site

21 Old sword
22 Witticism
23 Resident
   (suff.)
25 "Whose
   Honey
   —You?"
26 Not gross
28 Shoo!
32 Motif

34 On tiptoes
35 Consonant
37 Infuriated
39 Elysium
40 English
   river
42 June
   beetle·
43 Goddess
   (Lat.)

54

PUZZLE 55

ACROSS

1 Need
5 Precipice
10 Wimbledon winner (1975)
11 Porter
12 Benefit
13 Showy
14 Palestinian plain
15 Vapor
16 Cheat
17 Lounge
19 Anger
20 Ace in the —
21 Actor Alan
22 Unruffled
23 Deceives
24 Cut with an ax
25 Frayed
26 Destiny
27 Unwomanly
30 Hockey great
31 One (Ger.)
32 Antelope
33 Steps
35 Old lance
36 Bring to light
37 To be (Fr.)
38 Precept
39 Eur. river

DOWN

1 Toil
2 In unison
3 Child's toy
4 Purview
5 Suit fabric
6 Prison (sl.)
7 Scheherazade's tales
8 Impedes
9 Budding doctor
11 TV's Paladin
15 — the bill
18 Circuit
21 Forsaken
22 Chuckle
23 Ex-boxer, Billy
24 Storeroom
25 Midriff
27 Deserve
28 Entrap
29 More extensive
34 Frost
35 Six (It.)

PUZZLE 56

ACROSS

1 Was overly fond
6 Tennis great
11 French river
12 Dwell
13 Pro- creators
14 Sliced again
15 Pronoun
16 Gear tooth
18 Here (Fr.)
19 Revolve
21 Paddle
22 Russian hemp
23 Trouba- dour's instru- ment
24 Adjust the clock
26 Wooden match
27 Trees
28 Record
29 Chou En- —
30 Architec- tural block
32 Siamese coin
33 "Yes" vote
34 Burglarize

36 Giant
38 — bleu!
40 Tennis great
41 Oregon city
42 Compressed
43 Variant of Helen

DOWN

1 Receptacle
2 Willow

3 Horror- struck
4 Before
5 Discourse at length
6 Huge
7 Actor Vigoda
8 Cousin of a rat race
9 Tutor

10 Pensioner
17 Resident (suffix)
20 Affinities
23 "— for Life" (1956 film)
24 Kindred
25 Term in grammar
26 Dexterity

28 Actress Susan
30 Poet (1265-1321)
31 "Two Women" star
35 Sanctuary
37 Art (Lat.)
39 Indian mulberry

56

PUZZLE 57

ACROSS
1 Colorless
5 Confronted
10 Brain part
11 Mental attitude
12 Tidbits with sandwiches
14 "My — and Only"
15 Miscellany
16 "—Gotta Be Me"
17 Driveway substance
19 Exclude
20 Spoil
21 Elec. unit
22 Silk fabric
25 Boundaries
26 Israeli port
27 — of a gun
28 Garland
29 Spank
32 Colorado Indian
33 Suffix
34 Choler
36 Popular dish
39 Being
40 Different
41 Shabby
42 Prophet

DOWN
1 Pedestal part
2 Regretting
3 German river
4 French dance
5 Converging
6 Noachian craft
7 "Tempest" role
8 Ennoble
9 Dry regions
11 Underground worker
13 Old dance
18 Lady friend (Fr.)
21 Air
22 Hails
23 Nail polish remover
24 Italian seaport
25 Mining finds
27 Light-haired
29 Devoutness
30 French city
31 Expunge
35 German river
37 Caesar
38 Loser to DDE

57

PUZZLE 58

ACROSS

1 In '61 he hit 61 homers
6 Barren
10 Sports setting
11 Procreate
13 Ex Reds' catcher
15 Ex boxer Lee
16 DiMaggio
17 Ex Boston Bruin
18 Dr. Brown's dog hero
19 Kid of jazz
20 Life (comb. form)
21 Peer Gynt's mother
22 Scand. measure
23 Extra
26 Servige citizen
27 Irish seaport
28 Fixed charge
29 Priest's garb
30 Pronoun
31 — service
34 Oahu garland
35 Muslim name
36 Mrs. Cantor
37 Olivier in "The —"
40 Place
41 Pick up the check
42 Chi-chi
43 Premature

DOWN

1 —domo
2 Redolence
3 Medical term
4 Garter or Tabard
5 City in Calif.
6 Dublin's — Theatre
7 Amer. Indian tribe
8 Infamous
9 Denounced
12 Ruling seat
14 Days of —
21 Clumsy boat
22 Wonderment
23 Balances
24 Cornmeal mush
25 Judge
26 Set up in a series
28 Sensed
30 Tie-twiddling comic
31 Ship
32 Perfect
33 Individual
38 Consume
39 Author Levin

PUZZLE 59

ACROSS

1 Boatswain's whistle
5 Hardwood tree
9 Spoken
10 Retaliate
13 Actress Virna
14 Bicycle for two
15 Written letter
16 Medicine (abbr.)
17 Greek letter
18 Do penance
20 Nancy's mate
21 Panjandrums
23 — Scotia
24 Ward off
25 Stephen Vincent —
26 Ponce de —
27 Stringent
28 Sandy's cry
29 Brogan and wingtip
30 Lambkin's cry
31 Charged atom
32 Chance
35 Concurred
37 Dobbin's tresses
38 Return to custody
39 Sicilian city
40 Wait
41 European river

DOWN

1 Gdynia citizen
2 Eye part
3 Knightly encounter
4 Samuel's mentor
5 Eucharist plates
6 Circumvent
7 Man's nickname
8 Written
11 Recover
12 Spring forth
16 Shed feathers
19 Revolve
21 Coast near India
22 Too old
23 Snow field
25 — your toes (alerted)
27 Shabby
29 Italian city
33 One of the Brontes
34 Fruit
36 Devour
37 Indian farmer

PUZZLE 60

ACROSS

1 Dance
5 Mill material
10 Finished
11 Working cat
13 He played Lawrence of Arabia
15 Indigenous
16 Throw a ball
17 Fencing dummy
18 Eggs (Lat.)
19 Salesman
23 One kind of eye
24 French resort
25 Baseball's Peewee
26 Split
27 Chaplain
28 Hoosier wit
29 Never (It.)
30 Foot (prefix)
31 Evaluate
35 Coercion
38 Dross
39 Opera prince
40 Leon —
41 Jug

DOWN

1 Short air trip
2 Kiln

3 Greek mountains
4 Act peevish
5 Cleveland is one
6 Honey badger
7 Japanese statesman
8 Sojournment

9 Put on the tube
12 Gratify
14 Mature
19 Sonora shawls
20 Turn state's —
21 Simply adored to

22 New Guinea town
23 Moslem Easter
25 Elevate
27 French scientist
29 Lanza or Cuomo

32 Exude
33 — lily
34 Social climber
36 Bobby from Ontario
37 Prosecute

PUZZLE 61

ACROSS
1 Kind of beer
6 Stone paving block
10 Mountain crest
11 Role for Vivian Vance
13 —pole
14 Greek letter
15 Break bread
16 Commotion
18 "—Was I Born?"
19 Vegetable
21 Chemise border
22 Rock
23 Israeli dance
24 Famed musketeer
25 Early physician
26 British gun
27 —out (dealt)
28 Sunder
29 Nose and ice cream
30 Mindanao volcano
31 Reverence
32 Duffer's object
35 Religious adherent
37 Alex Haley's best seller
39 Kovacs
40 French city
41 Preeminent
42 Philippine island

DOWN
1 Recent
2 Venezuelan copper center
3 Mince no words
4 Summer (Fr.)
5 Endures
6 Assail
7 Anglo-Saxon letter
8 All pertinent facts
9 Leashed
12 Parishioner
17 John or Jane
20 Midday
22 Longtime Navy men
23 Detest
24 Scrape
25 Army VIP
27 Cut down
29 Service affairs
33 Coup d'—
34 To be (Lat.)
36 N.M. Indian
38 Mining find

61

PUZZLE 62

ACROSS

1 Faction
5 Heap
9 Perfect
11 Slanting
13 Spread joy
14 Pinch bar, e.g.
15 Crisscross
16 Famous "Stooge"
18 Midianite king
19 Kentucky city
21 Rich
22 Bulwer-Lytton heroine
23 Oz canine
24 Musical groups
26 "Two Women" star
27 Split
28 Gossip
29 Before
30 Developed canines
33 Alder tree
34 Neighbor of Ill.
35 Epoch
36 Halo wearer
38 Presbyter

40 Thai monetary unit
41 English novelist
42 Sandy hill
43 Watched

DOWN

1 Italian city
2 Stalls
3 Mann work

4 Consume
5 Blanched
6 Resident of (suff.)
7 Dearly await
8 Heighten
10 French city
12 Son of Poseidon
17 United

20 Mining find
23 Civil wrong
24 Beat one's —
25 Military tactic
26 German art songs

28 Snuggery
30 Championship
31 Opera conductor
32 Challenged
37 "Brandy —"
39 One of the Majors

PUZZLE 63

ACROSS
1 Visit
5 Engendered
10 Molding style
11 Greek moon goddess
12 Concourse
13 Blab
14 Hockey great
15 In favor
16 Vietnamese holiday
17 Drinking vessel
19 Exclamation
20 Designate
21 Dream (Fr.)
22 "Silkwood" co-star
23 Paul's companion
24 Snow goose genus
25 Claim
26 Trilby, e.g.
27 Servitude
30 Go wrong
31 Prior to
32 Container
33 Euphoric
35 Theatrical bit
36 Horsemen
37 Lug
38 Shabby
39 Southwest wind

DOWN
1 French painter
2 Plato's marketplace
3 Become skilled in
4 Directed
5 Manly symbol
6 Porker
7 Become adept in
8 Away from camp
9 Develop bicuspids
11 Fury
15 Klinger in "MASH"
18 Incisive
21 Regretted
22 Chan is one
23 Vocation
24 Drinking toast
25 House of —
27 "China Seas" star
28 "— Parisienne"
29 Gatecrash
34 Prepare ensilage
35 As written (Mus.)

PUZZLE 64

ACROSS

1 Diplomacy
5 Ciphered
10 Noisily
12 Do penance
13 Wind
  instrument
14 Hits from
  Berlin
15 Indian
  cymbals
16 Cat
  or chance
18 Prefix
  with cycle
19 Impetus
21 Needle-
  fish
22 Surmount
23 Burning
24 Pursuit
25 Rescued
26 Knowledge
27 German
  river
28 — had it!
29 Italian
  physicist
30 "Alice"
  character
31 Anglo-
  Saxon
  king
32 Society
  lass
35 Alaskan
37 Jalopy
39 Seed coat
40 Fortune-
  teller
  card
41 A Ford
42 Sicilian
  city

DOWN

1 —
  Hartley
  Act
2 "Rondo
  —Turca"
3 Was disin-
  terested
  (colloq.)
4 Egyptian
  king
5 Hindu
  social
  group
6 Sioux
7 See 3
  Down
8 Artisan
9 Requested
11 Corrupt
17 Cato's
  greeting
20 Level
22 Scooped up
23 Hold out
24 Atmosphere
25 Exclusive
27 Gained
29 Essential
33 Jacket
  or collar
34 Greek
  "B"
36 Colorado
  Indian
38 Scottish
  explorer

64

PUZZLE 65

ACROSS

1 Tokyo bar specialty
5 School course
9 Legal document
10 Fatty acid
12 Sicilian spewer
13 Complicate
15 Excavated
16 Wag
17 Child of Loki
18 Caustive
20 Roll of sawbucks
21 Penalty
22 Suffer from
23 Arbuckle
25 "Algiers" star
26 Yearn
27 Fastening device
28 American Indian
29 Flynn film
32 Spanish composer
33 "El —"
34 Literary tyke
35 Mason's need
37 Italian river
38 European river
39 Layer of paint
40 Feat
41 She (Fr.)

DOWN

1 Malmo citizen
2 — Rubinstein
3 Roger Miller song
4 Greek letter
5 Whodunit factor
6 Winged
7 Denary
8 Old TV police show
11 Split
14 Presbyter
16 Vinous
19 Location
22 One having guests
23 He sold his soul
24 Members of Equity
25 "Strike Up the —"
27 Saluted
29 Make the —
30 Ultimate
31 Chew the scenery
36 Bad news
37 Expert

PUZZLE 66

ACROSS
1 Enfant's mother
5 Ceiling supports
10 Cupid
11 Shrewd
13 Complacent
14 Victory symbol
15 Child of Loki
16 Future ham
17 Western state (abbr.)
18 Clarify
20 Three, in Napoli
21 Chinese society
22 Sultry songtress
23 Hind
24 Campus queen
25 Abound
26 Joust
27 —deal
28 —hygiene
30 Anglo-Saxon letter
31 Caddoan Indian
32 Faulty
34 Interpose
36 Napoleonic setting
37 Garment part
38 Chilling glance
39 Presbyter
40 Eyot

DOWN
1 Pulverize
2 Wheat variety
3 Casino cynosure
4 Work unit
5 Blanching
6 Indian tribe
7 Man's nickname
8 Reverse a trend
9 Guided
12 Young eel
16 "Turandot" character
19 Froth
22 Gun name
23 Seahawks' home
24 Movie (Sp.)
25 Lock of hair
26 Young one
28 Impel
29 Epithet
33 Challenge
35 Foot (prefix)
36 Hebrew for Lord

PUZZLE 67

ACROSS

1 Zhivago's love
5 Wild guess
9 Rose derivative
10 Knightly gear
12 She "mothered" 37 Across
15 Filled treat
16 "A Shropshire—"
17 Greek letter
18 Regard highly
20 Drop the bait
21 Some
22 Table d'—
23 Bret—
26 Budding star
27 Region
28 Intimate
29 Tatter
30 Arrived at O'Hare
33 Generation
34 Succor
35 African worm
37 Absurd misuse of words
40 Succinct
41 Particular
42 Legal document
43 Spanish cash

DOWN

1 Light item
2 Courtyards
3 Leveled
4 Fortify
5 Earnings
6 Do business
7 Elec. term
8 Ennui
11 Revolve
13 Set straight
14 Document
19 First name in spydom
22 Grasp
23 Pasha's passion
24 Biblical mountain
25 Treated lavishly
26 Certainly!
28 Coupled
30 Memory loss
31 Choice part
32 Medicinal draughts
36 Shooting stuff
38 Metric measure
39 Dilly

PUZZLE 68

ACROSS
1 French "java"
5 Creche setting
11 Chinese port
12 Melodic
13 Uncover
14 Stations
15 Skill
16 Grassy ground
17 Owed
18 Scottish entertainer
20 The Campbells, e.g.
21 Bardot film
22 Offend
23 Rozelle of football
24 Like some undies
25 More than satisfy
26 Enjoy the sun
27 Colored
28 Bell on film
31 Thor's stepson
32 Bikini part
33 — party
34 Fits the rudder
36 Hold out
37 Restlessness
38 Gaelic
39 "P" in V.I.P.
40 Hebrew measure

DOWN
1 Plotters
2 American soprano
3 Dealer in futures
4 Watch
5 Calif. city
6 Tract
7 Sip
8 Item for the superstitious
9 Sea inlet
10 Take umbrage
16 Consonant
19 Out of fashion
20 Chevy —
23 "Perils of —"
24 Tibetan monk
25 Pipe down!
26 Infertile
29 Region of Germany
30 Door sign
32 Senorita's kiss
35 Spanish article
36 Tolstoy

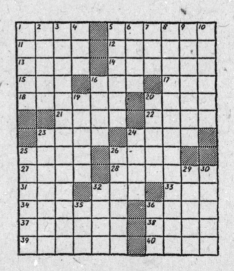

PUZZLE 69

ACROSS
1 Interlude
6 Cut off
11 Time waster
12 Net fabric
13 Name in N.Y.C. politics
15 Vocal note
16 Napoleonic marshal
17 Attitudinized
22 Cling
23 Salt tree
27 Queen (Fr.)
28 "The New Avengers" hero
29 English composer
30 "Shandy" author
31 Welles in "The—"
33 Harem room
36 Cadiz cheer
37 Boss Tweed, e.g.
43 Air spirit
44 By now boring
45 Shelf
46 Precipitous

DOWN
1 F'loor of exchange
2 Dean Martin film
3 German city
4 Ham's brother
5 Steno's error
6 Editor's concern
7 What's that?
8 Ardor
9 Auk genus
10 Depend upon
14 English river
17 Prefix for medic
18 European river
19 Climb
20 Principle
21 Passe
24 Tenure
25 Russian river
26 Heavenly Barbara
28 Scorsese's were "Mean"
30 Part of a doorway
32 According to—
33 Oct. birthstone
34 Challenge
35 Dry
38 Young sheep
39 Cunning
40 German article
41 Summer, in Dijon
42 Dem.'s opponent

69

PUZZLE 70

ACROSS

1 Oland film role
5 Cicatrix
9 Stringed instrument
10 Sir Gawain's garb
12 Cupid
13 Plundered
15 Diabolical
17 Gardner
18 Printing need
19 Man's nickname
20 Illinois city
24 Troll
25 Elicit
26 Dramatize
27 Snow field
28 Youngster
29 "We — Not Alone"
30 "I — Ideas"
31 Chatter
32 Dutch scholar
37 Bride on the run
39 Gist
40 Vaquero's rope
41 Seaweed extract
42 Pinafore
43 Regard as

DOWN

1 Suited
2 Scottish philosopher
3 Particle
4 Fiddler
5 Salty
6 Pot
7 I love (Lat.)
8 Service club member
11 Reprisal
14 Knife
16 Baseball team
20 Household
21 Generally
22 Popular TV vessel
23 ETO nickname
24 Sault — Marie
26 Bristle
28 Horror
30 Silly ones
33 Tropical fish
34 Birthmark
35 Compulsion
36 Join
38 Greek letter

70

PUZZLE 71

ACROSS

1 Shadow-box
5 Meander
9 Cheri's coffee
10 Lake or city
11 Dilettantish
12 Monopoly
15 Apis
16 Form for Dracula
17 English river
18 European river
20 W.W.II agency (abbr.)
21 Hidden
23 Journey
24 Pallid
25 Famous songstress
26 Let go
27 Plowed the waves
28 Lettuce
29 Work-pants fabric
30 Skill
31 Youth
32 Obtain
35 Resume
37 Engender
38 Interpret
39 Afr. fox
40 She had a lamb
41 Detail

DOWN

1 Strike-breaker
2 Trim
3 When things quiet down
4 King (Sp.)
5 Deny
6 Make a speech
7 Make public
8 Weather-wise one
13 Breathe out
14 Vaulted
16 German city
19 Pay attention to
21 E. Indian sailor
22 Off the ship
23 Attenuated
25 Forenamed
27 Sterne character
29 Obvious
33 Gaelic
34 Abound
36 Shade of green
37 Capuchin monkey

71

PUZZLE 72

ACROSS

1 Throb
5 Baby buggy
9 No—
   (airline
   term)
10 Fabled man
12 This way
   please
13 Outcome
15 Written
   letter
16 Distress
   call
17 Born (Fr.)
18 Barren
20 Color
21 Miffed
22 Sp. dollar
23 Vulgar
25 Less
   mannerly
26 Trust
27 Ninny
28 Do a sum
29 Measure
   out
32 Capuchin
   monkey
33 Cotter,
   e.g.
34 Malay
   gibbon
35 —route
37 Telegraph
38 Follow
   the scent
39 Behold
   (Lat.)
40 Maintain

41 Property
   transfer

DOWN

1 Camp-
   fire
   residue
2 Hope—
3 Wayne in
   "The—"
4 Lambkin's
   ma

5 Slammer
   release
6 Peewee
   or
   Della
7 Beast
8 R.C.M.P.
   members
11 I beg you!

14 Drift
16 Coward
   and
   Olivier
19 Optimistic
22 Heart (sl.)
23 Kentucky
   blue—
24 Blue-
   pencil

25 Nothing,
   in Paris
27 Gluey
29 Star
   in Virgo
30 Moliere's
   forte
31 Liberated
36 Late Cole
37 Espouse

72

PUZZLE 73

ACROSS
1 Inverness, e.g.
5 Wobble
11 English river
12 Unwilling
13 Tennyson poem
14 Jewelry weights
15 One (Ger.)
16 Writer Serling
17 Greek letter
18 Antique
20 Sheep tick
21 Song refrain
22 Appointment
23 Twenty
25 Sharpened
26 Civil wrong
27 Legal document
28 Caligula, e.g.(abbr.)
29 Weepy
32 Mindanao volcano
33 Building wing
34 Actress Miranda
35 City near Toledo, Ohio
37 Athletic group
38 — Tubbs
39 Seaweed
40 Put a new time on
41 German river

DOWN
1 Small carving
2 Help
3 As equals
4 Scope
5 Wash. city
6 Shun
7 Bard's adverb
8 Olympic category
9 Lover of beauty
10 Took quarters
16 Annoy
19 Filled pastry
22 Performer
23 Ship or clam
24 Liken
25 Restore to health
27 Cross out
29 Small anvil
30 Custom
31 Texas states man
36 My (Lat.)
37 P.I. peasant

73

PUZZLE 74

ACROSS
1 Failure
5 Premise
10 Path
11 Get lost!
   Last word
13 Blake of
   "Gunsmoke"
14 Err
15 Monk's title
16 Yellow
   ocher
17 Bread roll
19 Surfeit
20 Merriment
21 City of
   Manasseh
22 Cast off
23 Covers
24 French
   resort
25 Summon
26 Piece
   of work
27 Classify
30 Poker
31 Powdered
   lava
32 Rome's
   —Veneto
33 Responsible
35 Cleft
36 Alone in
   a crowd
37 Gaelic
38 Author
   Gide
39 Employer

DOWN
1 Liquid
   container
2 Vampire
3 Band's
   gig
4 Write
5 Pulpit
6 Moslem
   V.I.P.

7 D.H.Law-
   rence
   work
8 Writes
9 Old-time
   ship
11 Vermont
   city

15 Nourish
18 Silken
19 "Red — in
   the Sunset"
22 Otary
23 Whip
24 "Street-
   car" role

25 "—
   Jones"
28 Wash
29 Potato
31 German
   river
34 Jujube
35 Fire (Fr.)

74

PUZZLE 75

ACROSS

1 Brazilian seaport
5 Would-be Lothario
11 Mortgage
12 Breathe in
13 Turkish regiment
14 Heavy
15 Detective (sl.)
16 Danube tributary
17 — been taken!
18 Stick to
20 No ladies there
21 Weight allowance
22 Stringed instrument
23 Asian plain
24 Boatswain's whistle
25 Slough off
26 Liquid measure
27 Narrative
28 Yarn
31 Silkworm
32 Monk's title
33 Glutton
34 New York city
36 Arizona city
37 Marked with streaks
38 Hibernia
39 Property
40 "Victory" heroine

DOWN

1 Rio de La —
2 Troubled
3 Go all out
4 Black cuckoo
5 Cereal grass
6 Swiss writer
7 Shinto Temple
8 Was disgusted with
9 Glorify
10 Break a promise
16 Russian city
19 Wear away
20 David's weapon
23 Boston's river
24 — colada
25 Ship's derrick
26 Promenade
29 Violin bow conditioner
30 Guam seaport
32 Fuss over
35 Actress Balin
36 — Blanc

75

PUZZLE 76

ACROSS
1 Overfill
5 Colorado resort
10 Winged
12 Metrical pattern
13 Compare
14 Creme de la creme
15 Calpurnia's greeting
16 Fr. shooting match
18 Turf
19 Oral expert
21 Native mineral
22 Jaunty
23 Oklahoma city
24 Manitoba Indian
25 Chinese money
26 Crawford film
27 Actress Teri
28 Ninny
29 Italian pastry specialty
32 Sam in "Quincy"
33 Hawk parrot
34 Marsh
35 Biblical mountain
37 Communities
39 Smyrna fig
40 Spread joy
41 Embellishing line
42 Run along

DOWN
1 Dieter's lunch
2 Animated
3 Captured
4 Summer (Fr.)
5 Ward off
6 Salt (Fr.)
7 Stalag internee
8 Port. resort
9 Required
11 Complete
17 Adherent
20 Numerical suffix
23 Deserve
24 Spanish kingdom
25 Japanese wild dog
26 Labor concerns
27 Merry (Fr.)
29 Principal
30 Slow (mus.)
31 Map feature
36 Bel —
38 Danube tributary

76

PUZZLE 77

ACROSS
1 Amplifying device
6 Get going
11 Baffle
12 Poor bettor
13 Becomes weary
14 Color
15 Woman's name
16 Apex
18 Beverage
19 On the beach
21 Table scrap
22 Except
23 Reverie
24 Thwack
26 Was rampant
27 Hurt
28 —Hashanah
29 Lion (Lat.)
30 Style of diplomacy
33 Sioux
34 Weight
35 Hutton or Conway
36 Drive
38 "Lorna —"
40 —Bryant
41 Hot coal
42 Start afresh
43 Frail

DOWN
1 Boundaries
2 Existing
3 Positively! (sl.)
4 Dutch commune
5 Unruly
6 Incline
7 Sanskrit school
8 Properly
9 Other side
10 Handled
17 Poem
20 Overfill
23 Ship's rigging support
24 Star-gazer's Mount
25 Nail polish remover
26 Carouser
28 Greek "R"
30 Trifle
31 Like some coats
32 Corundum
37 Resident (suffix)
39 Noun suffix

PUZZLE 78

ACROSS

1 N. England river
5 Con game
9 Have in mind
10 Opposite
12 Ireland
13 Beyond repair
15 Statute
16 At one's mercy
17 Persevere
19 Fencing dummy
20 Work unit
21 E. Eur. people
22 Fall in folds
25 Stone marker
26 Rant
27 Bring — boil
28 Consumed
29 Fight with
33 Chopping finely
36 On the run
37 Yarn
38 Cheap bistro
39 Proceed
40 Incessant
41 Dwelling expense
42 Trust

DOWN

1 Utter
2 Texas city
3 Menu (Fr.)
4 Unified
5 Vaulted
6 Clever move
7 Landed (poet.)
8 Priest's vestment
11 Divulge
14 Search
16 Nucleus
18 Cantinflas film
21 Men only
22 Play
23 Classification
24 Vindicator
25 "— Sung Blue"
27 Inhabit
30 Existing
31 Judge's symbol
32 Corundum
34 — d'Azur
35 Golf club
38 German article

PUZZLE 79

ACROSS
1 Mexican coin
5 Deer
9 Engrossed
10 Opposite
12 Gunther's "Inside —"
13 Rob or Fritz
15 Haunt
16 Cover
17 African beast
18 Gaffers
20 Turkish flag
21 Famed director
22 — lily
23 Mountain crest
25 Part of a stair
26 Masculine
27 Hindu holy man
28 Along in years
29 Carefree
32 Outfit
33 — had it!
34 Penpoint
35 Wool type
37 Vegetable (var.)
38 Prosper
39 Acute
40 Tooth (Fr.)

41 Whirlpool

DOWN
1 Spanish museum
2 Artist's need
3 Lanky
4 Japanese river
5 "— Has Sprung"

6 — the mark (behaved)
7 Muslim name
8 Leggy
11 Quit cold
14 Hearsay

16 Smooth consonant
19 Paired
20 Out of the way
23 Soprano Lucine
24 Turbulent
25 Evaluate

27 Scholar
30 Fathered
31 Black
33 Inflexible
36 Resident (suffix)
37 Turk. weight measure

79

PUZZLE 80

ACROSS
1 Hurt
5 Ratchet part
9 Fix eggs
11 African plants
13 Courtyard
14 Lead-tin alloy
15 "Little —Echo"
16 Deep-sea
18 Mailer
20 Pagoda ornament
21 Masticate
22 "On Golden —"
23 Old World falcon
25 Shade of gray
26 Syrian bishop's title
27 Por —!
28 China's late Chairman
29 Do a slow burn
31 Brass instrument
33 French "friend"
35 Copter blade
36 Lowest point
38 Win by —
39 Corn meal mush
40 Cuchulain's wife
41 Daunted

DOWN
1 Snakes
2 Fetter
3 Drop all the way
4 Silkworm
5 Eucharist plate
6 Athena's title
7 Frazzled
8 Merciful
10 Boarder
12 Leave the Union
17 Crow's sound
19 S.A. bird
22 Scheme
23 Winged tree seed
24 Edible mollusk
25 Brownish color
27 German article
29 More painful
30 Rousseau book
32 Stockings
34 Exacer-bated
37 One —time

80

PUZZLE 81

ACROSS
1 Glut
5 Follow-up drink
11 Damson, e.g.
12 Evacuate
13 English river
14 Individually operated
15 Snuggery
16 Medico
17 Dutch township
18 Twist together
20 Drumstick
21 Gets skittish
22 Shelter
23 Wee pig
24 Jabber
25 Mort —
27 Spy in Canaan
29 First mate
30 Set forth
32 Turmeric
33 Before (prefix)
34 Prefix for cycle
35 Resident M.D.
37 Film sleuth
38 Greek market-places
39 Guest (Fr.)
40 Clemency
41 Brutus' highway

DOWN
1 Fictional sleuth
2 Space people
3 Cause trouble
4 Uncle (dial.)
5 Sings like Crosby
6 In the future
7 Soul (Fr.)
8 Monroe film
9 Ducked out on
10 Back out
16 Count calories
19 Legal document
22 Place for McGee's closet
24 Harvard's rival
25 Old Sat. afternoon feature
26 Vindicate
27 He played Norton
28 Tongue-lash
30 Youngster
31 Railroad car
36 "— Tu?" (Verdi aria)
37 Greek letter

81

PUZZLE 82

ACROSS

1 Yemen's capital
5 Confederate of Absalom
10 Expectant
11 Congressional —
13 Moon feature
14 Sapient
15 Carpenter, e.g.
16 Skill
17 Sesame
18 Stadium cheer
19 Ovine cry
20 Laughing sound
21 Joust
23 None better
24 Kind of cake
26 Strong point
27 King of comedy
28 Daydream
29 Child of Loki
30 Barnyard sound
31 Obstruct
34 M.D.'s group
35 — hat
36 Epoch
37 Be contingent

39 Drudge
40 Turkish capital
41 Wagnerian role
42 Candle
43 Equal

DOWN

1 Philippine island
2 Guam seaport
3 John Wayne film
4 Grow mellow
5 Mountain in Turkey
6 Famous D.C. hostess
7 Vaudeville group
8 Dixie charmer
9 Most Bohemian
12 Strike out
16 Talented
22 Hostel
23 Scary cry
24 Afr. desert
25 Merciful

26 Nourishment
28 Hungarian playwright
30 Victor or Roger
32 Ascended
33 Electronic sentinel
38 Faucet
39 Vigor

82

PUZZLE 83

ACROSS

1 Commission earners
6 Bugle call
10 Overhead
11 Old French decree
13 Italian film star
14 Gaze
15 Singular
16 Dancing great
18 Beak
19 Plaything
20 Saint (Sp.)
21 Jacket style
23 Apportion
24 Turkish coin
26 Bishop's headdress
27 Revolve
28 Insect
29 Time period
30 Lamentable
31 Midianite king
34 Guide an aircraft
36 Author Deighton
37 Rope fiber
38 Clipped off
40 Happening
41 Succinct
42 Nervous
43 Sequence

DOWN

1 Drawing room
2 Residence
3 Hallelujah!
4 Night before
5 Legislator
6 Sapid
7 Greek river
8 Hallelujah!
9 Notched (bot.)
12 Adolescent
17 Scion
22 First-down yardage
23 With (Ger.)
24 Relaxed
25 Come through it
26 Calif. city
28 Door —
30 Saline
32 Metrical pattern
33 Spiritual
35 Chain —
39 "Leave — to Heaven"

PUZZLE 84

ACROSS

1 Italian river
5 Violent
10 — Rogers St. Johns
12 Mistreat
13 Uses the telephone
14 Concise
15 Speck
16 Watch out!
18 Hair wave
20 Allegiance
21 Attention
22 "The Perfect Fool"
23 Subsequently
25 Suspend
26 Onion's kin
27 Fashion
28 Generation
29 French city
32 Indict
34 Capture
36 Believer in God
37 Type style
39 Nine (comb. form)
40 Complete
41 Dignified
42 Valley

DOWN

1 "Shane" star
2 Phrase
3 Charro's rope
4 Badly
5 Assessment
6 At rest
7 Actress, Ellen —
8 Distributing
9 Become profound
11 Depth bomb (sl.)
17 Bard's adverb
19 Exude
22 Divining rod
23 Earthly
24 Audition
25 Wasp
26 Chieftain
27 Young sheep
29 Needful
30 Join forces
31 Brazilian seaport
33 On a cruise
35 Signal
38 Israeli airport

PUZZLE 85

ACROSS

1 Lumpkin
5 False show
9 Italia's capital
10 — operandi
12 Romanian city
13 Turkish inn
15 Banker
17 Mount discourse (abbr.)
18 Spire ornament
19 Steep slopes
23 Mouth (sl.)
24 Integrity
25 San —, Calif.
26 Greek peak
27 Toasted
28 Resident (suff.)
29 Haggard novel
30 Became established
36 Racine drama
37 Olive genus
38 More cunning
39 "...angels — to tread"
40 Spot
41 Gerald or Henry

DOWN

1 Study, in a way
2 Monk parrot
3 Where Muscat is
4 Florida county
5 Shows pleasure
6 Slugger's feat
7 Muslim prayer call
8 Cain, e.g.
11 Oozing
14 Camera stand
16 French river
19 Prefer
20 Party giver
21 Confuse
22 Burnt —crisp
23 Aunt (Sp.)
25 Feat
27 Spanish wine
29 Slumber
31 "—Can't Be Love"
32 Take off, as a hat
33 Margarine
34 Fray
35 Anc. ointment

PUZZLE 86

ACROSS

1 Skein of yarn
5 Sty
8 Wahine's dance
9 Vinegar
13 Dry
14 Bring back
15 Get — of
16 Of Rome
17 Corrupt
19 Mobster's gun
20 Actress, Charlotte —
21 Presidential "no"
22 A must with lox
25 Less common
26 French "she"
27 — Aviv
28 Brazilian tree
29 "The — and I" (1940 song)
32 Relatives
34 Actress Balin
36 Football play
37 Dressed
38 Take umbrage at
39 Land measure
40 Trouble
41 At that time

DOWN

1 Burn
2 Startling
3 Slur over
4 Much cash
5 Prison release
6 Smyrna figs
7 Russian river
10 A Rogers
11 Fly
12 Clergyman
16 Iranian coin
18 On the house
21 Singer Jerry
22 Lab vessel
23 Lofty
24 Adrenal and others
25 Beatty in "Reds"
27 Thirty (Fr.)
29 Conductor Walter
30 Zero (sl.)
31 Finnish lake
33 Sketched
35 Yemen port
37 Tin-roof prowler

86

PUZZLE 87

ACROSS

1 Talk
5 Preservative
9 Song refrain
10 Sleuth's findings
12 English essayist
13 Revolve
15 High note
16 Disinfectant ingredient
17 Flee
19 "Quincy" co-star
20 Carney
21 Surrounded by
22 Gregorian, e.g.
25 Newspaper article
26 Ace in the —
27 Seal herd
28 Building annex
29 Best duds
32 Absconding
34 Consume
36 Uprising
37 Reminder
38 Ward off
39 Eternally
40 Anatomical network
41 Bivouac need

DOWN

1 Shropshire hills
2 German city
3 Assumed name
4 Chinese pagoda
5 Writing
6 Secluded
7 Pear-shaped instrument
8 British ritual
11 Radio interference
14 Wear away
16 Segment
18 Bastinado
21 Assistant
22 College yell
23 Shout
24 Finished
25 "Turandot" role
27 Rudder part
29 — mignon
30 He played "Superman"
31 Mandarin's office
33 English essayist
35 Civil wrong
37 "Hail, fellow, well —"

87

PUZZLE 88

ACROSS

1 Yemen's capital
5 Nimbus
10 Smell
11 Songbird
13 Polish cake
14 Dodger
15 Conceit
16 Pompey's greeting
17 Dutch commune
18 Fiery
19 German article
20 Turmeric
21 Time period
23 Trial run
24 Excitement
26 Substantial
27 Solitary
28 Vegetables
29 Before
30 Crazy
31 Chatter
34 Epoch
35 Have debts
36 New Mexican Indian
37 Noxious insects
39 Endure
40 Unabridged
41 "— Kleine Nacht-musik"
42 "— Faces of Eve"
43 Valley

DOWN

1 Earnest
2 Maxim
3 Not a soul here
4 Macaw
5 Adroit
6 Kind of sausage
7 "— Clear Day"
8 Moving smoothly
9 Most abstruse
12 Compact
16 Mankind's father
22 Sooner than
23 Beverage
24 Garment feature
25 Outburst
26 Iranian's ancestor
28 Oklahoma Indian
30 Watered fabric
32 French river
33 Eucharist plate
38 Me (Ger.)
39 Table part

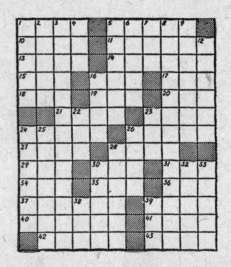

PUZZLE 89

ACROSS

1 Heroic tale
5 Watercourse
9 Czech river
10 Meal
12 Vatican office
13 Sagacious
14 Indefinite period
15 Life (Fr.)
16 Haggard novel
17 Consummate performer
19 Vietnamese holiday
20 Bulwer-Lytton heroine
21 Ceremony
22 Squander
24 French school
25 Toward shelter
26 Burn
27 Nigerian
28 Pudding thickener
30 Greek letter
31 Small fish
32 Wire measure
34 Seduce
36 Titled lady
37 Brawler
38 Golf club
39 From a distance
40 Gumbo

DOWN

1 Withered
2 Marketplace for Plato
3 Hit home
4 Altar constellation
5 Readjust
6 Likely
7 Biting comment
8 Lover of beauty
10 Hoist
11 Squirrel monkey
15 Creeping plant
18 Lug
21 "—'s Daughter"
22 Diner's call
23 Iron Curtain land
24 Consonant
26 Passover meal
28 Kitchen gadget
29 Indonesian island
33 Russian river
35 Call—day
36 God (Ital.)

PUZZLE 90

ACROSS
1 Showed all
6 Slender
10 St. Johns
11 Aplomb
12 Track-
    betting
    feature
14 Marine bird
15 Indian
    cymbals
16 Shriek
    of fright
17 News feature
19 Deli item
22 Match
25 Mountain
    crest
26 Tree or nut
27 Navy woman
28 Jury lists
29 Playwright
    Albee
31 Fish
33 Go wrong
34 Overwhelm
    (sl.)
37 One way
    to live
40 Type of
    beer
41 Item for
    judging
42 Gov't
    agents
43 Bring
    to bear

DOWN
1 Proffered
2 Jewish
    month
3 Leather
    product
4 Building
    addition
5 Dracula's
    latent
    period
6 French coin

7 Break
    the bonds
8 Emerald —
9 Submissive
11 Survey
13 Surrealist
17 Pre-
    ordained
18 Rectify
19 Maxim
20 Constel-
    lation

21 Influence
23 Such
    (Fr.)
24 Raised
    railroads
26 Gunfire
28 Role
30 Finery
31 Wisdom
    symbol

32 First
    name
34 Take a
    mate
35 Hebrew
    measure
36 Whip
    mark
38 Craving
39 Assess

90

PUZZLE 91

ACROSS

1 Like yesterday's rose
6 Upright
11 Out of the way
12 Univ. of Maine site
13 Refuse
15 Norse war god
16 Beat time
17 Wise about
18 Nickel nurser
20 Be generous
23 Chief
27 Worship
28 Burn
29 Feeling blue
30 Lime tree
31 Rousseau work
33 Liquor
36 — long
37 Greek letter
40 Having trouble
43 "House boat" star
44 Task (var.)
45 Foeman
46 Consumed

DOWN

1 Reality
2 Pale
3 Designing name
4 Taro root
5 Defiance
6 Card game
7 Florentine gold
8 Torch singer, Lillian —
9 Price paid
10 Chicago area
14 Assuage
18 French river
19 "Watch on the —"
20 Pop
21 Early Fr. king
22 At this time
24 Scope
25 Mature
26 Lair
28 Suppress
30 Italian river
32 Late labor leader
33 "— Britannia"
34 Atop
35 Moon area
37 State (Fr.)
38 Radial, e.g.
39 Symbol of Ra
41 Jewel
42 Asian sheep

PUZZLE 92

ACROSS
1 Afr. country
5 Stash
10 Adored one
11 Distillery mixes
12 Court matter
13 Classify
14 Ripen
15 Somewhat
16 Blue grass
17 "Will Penny" star
19 — and image
20 French river
21 Yearn
22 Old-time dagger
23 Bacchus is its god
24 British gun
25 Bell
26 Trying time
27 Good for growing
30 Alkali
31 Soul (Fr.)
32 — Fail
33 Oleic acid salt
35 Arboreal growth
36 With much love
37 Ironwood tree
38 Jockey Arcaro
39 — out (got by)

DOWN
1 Heb. prophet
2 Old saying
3 Becomes unnerved
4 O'Neill play
5 Assign actors
6 Ninny
7 Execution site
8 Gallant Ms.
9 Inheritance
11 Lumber State
15 Os, for one
18 English river
19 Thorn (Lat.)
22 Hardened
23 Had on
24 Walked
25 Full of pluck (var.)
28 Thread
29 Alleviated
31 Salt tree
34 Onassis
35 Woman's name

PUZZLE 93

ACROSS

1 Speed of sound
5 Waikiki adieu
10 Yen
11 Swamp
13 Stain
14 Stir the passions
15 Macaw
16 Combat pilot
17 Little Alonso
18 Staying place
19 Apiece
20 Shrewmouse
21 —whiz!
23 A continent (Fr.)
24 Inventor
26 Cut off, as fleece
27 Russian sea
28 Holbrook
29 We (It.)
30 Fit— fiddle
32 Viper
35 Duke (Fr.)
36 Liquor
37 Old Chinese kingdom
38 On terra firma
40 Bavarian river
41 Vital
42 Procreator
43 Brinker did
44 Ancient Asian

DOWN

1 African people
2 Oak's fruit
3 Late Chinese leader
4 Child of Loki
5 Priest's garment
6 Anti-social one
7 Killer whale
8 Late Ethiopian leader
9 Oregon city
12 Return to —
16 Mimic
22 Conger
23 So that's it!
24 Extinct tribe
25 Stimulates
26 Pretense
30 Fr. law decree
31 Leather
33 Pottery fragment
34 Soupy food
39 Seraglio chamber
40 Political cause

PUZZLE 94

ACROSS
1 After its day
6 Auto style
11 "Striking" place
12 Living
13 Narrow escapes
15 Nautical chain
16 Grassland
17 Pianist Tatum
18 Compassion
20 Famous Jack
23 Fine dress
27 Enflame
28 Comfy state
29 Register
31 Capital of Morocco
32 Storehouse
34 Lamentable
37 Break bread
38 Likely
41 Suspenseful serial
44 Eagle's abode
45 Rich cake
46 Turn aside
47 Blot out

DOWN
1 Covenant
2 Unite
3 Fruit
4 His (Fr.)
5 Small hole
6 Bogart film
7 Old note
8 Prima donna
9 Assert
10 Hotbed
14 Vast area
18 Abominated
19 Sometimes Dutch
20 Haggard work
21 Write
22 Traitor
24 Mortar mixer
25 Pretty —picture
26 Up to now
30 Jacket
31 Revolve
33 Nonsense!
34 Tropical fish
35 Toward shelter
36 Gossip
38 Indian city
39 Favorites
40 Corner
42 Shame on you!
43 And not

94

PUZZLE 95

ACROSS

1 Ship's jail
5 Pick up the marbles
8 Stratagem
9 Moorish tomtom
13 Resound
14 Card sequence
15 Shinto temple
16 Muffin
17 Tea variety
18 Bank employee
20 Flail
21 Dregs
22 Insincere talk
23 Less available
25 Dance
26 Wife of Cuchulain
27 Shade of yellow
28 Household members
29 Coat or jacket
32 Indeed! in Antrim
33 But (Lat.)
34 Palm leaf
35 Abrasion
37 Salver

38 Sinew
39 — Klemperer
40 Ending for doctor
41 In those days

DOWN

1 French seaport
2 Dress trimming
3 MacArthur quote
4 Earth (comb. form)
5 Ethel —
6 Newspaper bit
7 "Brandy —"
10 Constantly on the move
11 In pain
12 Shed

16 He was Grandpa Walton
19 Certain looks
20 Surmount
23 Food
24 Punish by mulct
25 Kicked along

27 Lorne or Graham
30 Fill with joy
31 Man-made fabric
33 Notice
36 Hayward film
37 Wee one

PUZZLE 96

ACROSS

1 Late states-
 woman
5 Rubbish
10 Monster
11 Deny
13 Zone
14 Go by
15 Egyptian
 deity
16 Earnings
17 Foamy
 drink
18 Jewish
 month
20 Tete-a-tete
21 Numerous
22 Manon aria
 "La—"
23 Role for
 Burt Ward
25 TV Marine
26 Incessant
27 Polish
 title
 of address
28 Marine bird
29 Future
 indica-
 tions
31 Weapon
32 Shed tears
33 — whiz
35 Ankara inn
37 Disorderly
38 Thin
 layer
39 Cathedral
 section

40 Brazilian
 seaport
41 Colored

DOWN

1 Castle
 feature
2 White heron
3 Irene Dunne
 film
4 Turmeric

5 Peace pact
6 Have
 faith in
7 Peruvian
 river
8 Hochner
 best seller
9 Subjugate
12 Vacillate

16 Famous
 Quaker
19 Scottish
 child
20 Beldam
23 A way to sell
24 Supervisor
25 Plucky
 (var.)

27 Entrance
30 Tennis
 term
32 Roman
 meal
34 Watched
36 Slower
 (mus.)
37 Plus

96

PUZZLE 97

ACROSS

1 Exhausted
6 Diaphanous
11 Falsify
12 Golf term
13 Dinner treat
15 Three —match
16 Stowe character
17 Speck
18 Unoriginal
20 Othello, e.g.
23 High spirits
27 Passion
29 Bequest recipient
30 Kind of grass
32 "Mild-mannered reporter"
33 Scout or Silver
35 Somewhat (suff.)
38 A.A. prospect
39 Dilly
42 Musical instrument
45 More than average
46 One of Noah's birds
47 Witch of —
48 Corundum

DOWN

1 N.H. river
2 Contrivance
3 Spirit lamp
4 Man's nickname
5 German city
6 Calmed down
7 Lincoln's secretary
8 Minced oath
9 Elsie's calf
10 Remainder
14 Diabolical
18 One's pledged word
19 Elicit
20 Deface
21 Rich rock
22 Unmatched
24 Common suffix
25 Number for Moses
26 Though
28 "— Cogburn" (Wayne film)
31 Stage item
34 Accumulate
35 Ait
36 Trumpeter
37 Crowd
39 Lay concrete
40 Caesar's highway
41 "—Boy"
43 Conceit
44 Cap

97

PUZZLE 98

ACROSS
1 Have debts
4 Nautical fastener
8 Keeley Smith's late mate
10 Son of Jacob
12 Consumed
13 Cubic meter
14 Anglo-Saxon letter
15 Haw and —
17 Husbands
18 Gratified
20 Emmet
21 Russian city
22 Isinglass
23 Jogs
25 Jury list
26 Warren Beatty film
27 Soft mineral
28 Participle ending
29 Don't interfere (sl.)
32 Jujube
33 Slower (mus.)
34 One (Fr.)
35 Cognizant
37 Gold braid
39 Shoelace
40 Breeding places
41 Liberal faction
42 Spelling match

DOWN
1 Speechify
2 Ungrudgingly
3 Uncle (dial.)
4 Established
5 Adherent (suff.)
6 Gourmand's delight
7 Roman playwright
8 Equal
9 Schemes
11 Certain revenue
16 Lamprey
19 — and crafts
22 Brewery need
23 Of a nomadic people
24 New effort
25 George C. Scott film
27 Parson bird
29 Baseball's George
30 Confederate
31 Hardy heroine
36 Ump
38 Johnny —

98

PUZZLE 99

ACROSS

1 Effrontery
5 Outburst
10 Potpourri
11 Halt
13 Do in
14 Awaken
15 Chinese dynasty
16 Before (prefix)
17 However (var.)
18 New York river
20 All — up
21 Coal scuttle
22 Limiting mark
23 Facilitate
26 Beyond its prime
27 Interlaced
28 Indian weight
29 Muslim male name
30 Missive
33 Youngster
34 Eggs (Lat.)
35 Large barrel
37 Wound slightly
39 Subside
40 Obstruct
41 Advantage
42 Accumulate
43 Regard

DOWN

1 Golly be!
2 Islamic diety
3 Climbing vine
4 Myrna —
5 Inviolable
6 Preamble
7 Weapon
8 Grew canines
9 Beauty lover
12 Blared
16 Persevere
19 So. Korean statesman
22 Shopping place
23 Fabric sample
24 North Star
25 Manifest
26 Greek cheese
28 Stringent
30 Bad bet
31 Circumvent
32 Scope
36 Abound
38 Turmoil
39 Espouse

99

PUZZLE 100

ACROSS

1 Canaanite deity
5 Pulverize
9 She (Fr.)
10 Cathedral setting
12 Faction
13 Worked long hours
15 Night before
16 Pop singer, George —
17 Taro root
18 Not tough
20 Lament
21 Nest-egg acct.
22 A Bronte
23 French novelist
26 Greek island
27 Solar disk
28 Greek letter
29 Fruit
30 Justification
34 City in Finland
35 "I — Rhythm"
36 All for
37 Alehouse
39 Dormouse
40 Walk (sl.)
41 Utah city
42 Printing process
43 Anatomical tissue

DOWN

1 Assail
2 — and kicking
3 Priscilla's John
4 Sonstress Brenda
5 Hebrew O.T. notes
6 Associate
7 El stop
8 Drinking invitation
11 Insect
14 Bequest recipient
16 Swiss city
19 Keaton
20 "West Side Story" girl
23 Egyptian statesman
24 Moorish drum
25 Surmount
26 First name
28 Without delay (sl.)
31 Seedlike body
32 Window style
33 Bellini opera
35 "True —"
38 Conceit
39 Destiny

PUZZLE 101

ACROSS
1 Do in
5 Child care expert
10 Sundered
11 Leash
13 Diabolical
14 Dress
15 Reprieve
17 Publication (sl.)
18 Before
19 Falstaff's title
20 Summer (Fr.)
21 Oklahoma Indian
22 Hibernia
23 Allude
26 English river
27 Arab official
28 "—Rosenkavalier"
29 Wall (Fr.)
30 Father and son
31 Weaken
34 Eyot
35 Set in motion
37 Texas river
39 Binge
40 Like some bases
41 Mangano film
42 Live

43 Scoundrel

DOWN
1 Cubic meter
2 Inamorata
3 Rebel
4 Shrill bark
5 Dormant
6 Benchley or Sellers

7 Baseball great
8 Bishop's garment
9 Horny tissue
12 London street
16 Bavarian river

21 Indian weight
22 Do wrong
23 Neglectful
24 Follow suit
25 Furnace chamber
26 Pavilion, e.g.
28 Adequate

30 Persian prophet
31 European river
32 Expiate
33 Corolla segment
36 Western state
38 Asian river

101

PUZZLE 102

HORIZONTAL

1—Make ready for surgery
5—Acid found in apples
10—Holding device
15—War god
19—Wander
20—One of the Muses
21—Cripples
22—Spend them in Venice
23—Hebrew measure
24—Gaseous element
25—Florida city
26——— of Wight
27—To sweat
28—Caverns
31—Required
33—Hebrides island
34—Dogma
35—Gudrun's husband
36—Immediately
39—Pub game
40—Incinerates
44—Some are collected
45——— Doone
46—French river
47—Indian
48—Turkish officers
49—Book by Poe
50—Arrives
51—To boss
52—Perched
53—Expenses
54—A color
55—Groups of footless animals
56—Raises
58—Minute sun spots
59—Former Chief Justice
60—Persian poet
61—Drawing room
62—Father
63—Mount in Palestine
66—Spartan serf
67—Lacking rhythm
71—Use
72—Lodge doorkeeper
73—A color
74—Constellation
75—Pith
76—Gold Moslem coin
77—Venetian magistrates
78—Worry
79—Moot gift
80—Ire
81—Discharges
82—Coat with tin-lead alloy
83—Detailed personal records
85—Bangs
86—Orison
87—Greek mountain
88—English dramatist
89—Wing-like
90—Plugs with a spigot
93—The youngest son
94—Charts advance course
98—Peruvian mountain wind
99—Greek market place
101—Aida, for one
103—Level
104—Fish sauce
105—Greek physician
106—Nostrils
107—Graceful garment
108—German admiral
109—Mr. Kefauver
110—The choice part
111—Slide

VERTICAL

1—Support
2—It has seven hills
3—Always
4—Continues firmly
5—Breed of sheep
6—The palm cockatoo
7—To load
8—Japanese name
9—Business establishments
10—Sections of garlic
11—Shoestring
12—Chalices
13—Honey
14—Books containing the Psalms
15—Girl's name
16—Hazard
17—Mr. Gardner
18—Germ
28—Kitchen utensils
30—Pilaster
32—Egyptian singing and dancing girl
34—Biblical weeds
35—Arabian gazelle
36—Leek-green quartz
37—Small portable organ
38—Growing out
39—Simpletons
40—States of unconsciousness
41—Private instructor
42—Musical study
43—Site of 1870 battle
45—Optical maser
46—Sophia
49—The sum
50—French painter
51—A frolic
53—"Ship of the desert"
54—Hue
55—Brother of Moses
57—An emetic
58—Less colorful
59—Rubs off
61—Word in the Psalms,
62—Dirks
63—Enclosed
64—Dispatch boat
65—Grates
66—Inklings
67—Impels
68—Linger
69—Miss Dunne
70—Provide food
72—Pope's triple crown
73—Singer Eydie
76—Method of training horses
77—Listen for it
78—Intrepid
80—Sage
81—Run away
82—Ensnare
84—Comfort
85—Certain autos
86—Gratify
88—"Gay ——"
89—Sovereign's decree
90—Saratoga Springs, et al.
91—Soft pith
92—Arrow poison
93—Young horse
94—Fairy
95—Grandparental
96—St. Philip
97—A shred
100—Xenon
102—Chum

PUZZLE 103

HORIZONTAL

1—American author
5—American novelist
10—American novelist
15—Venomous serpent
19—Black
20—Ocean vessel
21—————— space
22—Jewish month
23—South ————
24—Enroll
25—Wife of Menelaus
26—Observe
27—Guidance
29—American humorist
31—Sameness
33—Network
34—Trap
36—European river
37—Comes to an end
40—Hunting dogs
42—Camera support
46—King of Judea
47—American author
48—Not pos.
50—High home
51—Emerald Isle
52—Fatigued
53—Certain boundaries
55—Spanish dining hall
56—Family member
57—Italian physicist
58—Kind of trunk
60—Lair
61—Abounded
63—Growing out
65—A roundworm
67—Heraldic bearing
69—Inexperienced
71—Similar
72—Bric-a-brac containers
76—Lamprey fisherman
78—Found in a kitchen
82—Crone
83—Pupil
85—Yawns
87—Son of Gad
88—A metal
90—Military caps
91—Ensigns of authority
92—Mythical king of Britain
93—Divest
95—Decompose
96—Saltpeter
97—Hackneyed
98—Fixture of afternoon party
100—Not crude
102—Resounded
103—Olive genus
105—Fast-moving
106—Cup's rim
107—Copes
111—Doctrine
112—Post Office items
116—Turkish regiment
117—Hue
119—Roman roads
121—Eat poi at this
122—Whirl
123—Sultan's decree
124—Frigid, Torrid, etc.
125—Grafted (Her.)
126—Far: comb. form
127—Biblical outcast
128—Corundum
129—Printer's mark

VERTICAL

1—American socialist
2—Countenance
3—Not any
4—American playwright
5—Bearing blocks
6—Articulated joint
7—Poker stake
8—Bishopric
9—Errant deed
10—To cleave
11—Regret
12—Gudrun's husband
13—Indigent
14—Also called "Papa"
15—Soldiers on guard
16—Word from the Cross
17—Stroke on the green
18—Weaver's reed
28—Marsh grass
30—Facts
32—Tiber tributary
34—Scorching
35—Man's nickname
37—Coffer
38—Uncanny
39—Ascend
40—Disgrace
41—Not a coupe
43—Madrid boulevard
44—Lubricated
45—American diplomatist
47—Poet's word
49—Coupled
52—Matrimony
53—Refined pig iron
54—Arabs
57—Flowerless plants
58—An ox
59—Roues
62—Witty saying
64—Regions
66—Grown in Assam
68—Anesthetic
70—Nullified
72—Early bridge
73—American author
74—Greek market place
75—Stupor
77—Sped
79—Danger
80—Declaim
31—Pronged
84—Measure of capacity
86—Through
89—Injurious to health
91—Belittle
92—Rough, prickly shrubs
94—Whine childishly
96—Pinches
97—European linden
99—Office need
101—More comely
102—Finicky
104—Worship
106—More exposed
107—Throw
108—Leather flask
109—To secure
110—Strike
112—Word on "the wall"
113—Family member
114—Portal
115—Hard fat
118—Poem
120—Male turkey

PUZZLE 104

HORIZONTAL

1—Intrigue
6—Preserves
11—Halley's, for one
16—White Spanish wine
17—Pungent bulb
18—Disclosed
20—University study group
21—Large ruminant
22—Deters
24—Fruit drink
25—Hard
27—Attach
29—Spigot
30—Character in "Dr. Zhivago"
32—Old Norse work
33—Peel
34—Gourd fruit
35—Bridge triumphs
37—Large paddles
39—Function in trigonometry
40—Sandpiper
41—Ancient ascetic
43—Dissolving
45—Dance step

46—Tidy
48—Accomplishing
49—Emblem of Wales
50—Overcame
54—Label
55—Saviour
59—Exclamation
60—Scourge
62—The aftersong
64—Half: a prefix
65—Chem. workshop
66—Friend, in Paris
67—Mr. Burrows
68—Caesar
69—A king of Judah
71—Overact
73—Resplendence
75—Poker stake
76—Revolution
78—Famous general
80—Barren (poetic)
82—Mountain lake
83—Locations
85—Thin bird
86—Cunning
89—Bears witness

91—Seats, of a kind
95—Cognizant
96—Merriment
97—Devours
99—Swagger
100—Food staple
101—Down in the dumps
102—Bark cloth
104—Chinese: comb: form
105—Make choice
106—Hikes
108—A color
110—Masonic group (abbr.)
111—Cried, as a horse
113—Excess of solar year
115—Famous musical
117—Garment part
118—French river
119—Card holding
120—Sea birds
121—Parisian heads
122—List of candidates

VERTICAL

1—Vaulted chambers
2—Fourth caliph
3—Proscribes
4—Size of type
5—Texas city
6—Seized roughly
7—Sole
8—Inlet
9—Physical disorder
10—Crackling
11—Stick together
12—Think
13—Repair
14—Omega
15—Seesaws
16—Sometimes won
19—Arranges in folds
20—Mud volcano
23—Uttered
26—A cheese
28—A three
31—Catkins
34—Pointed
36—Dirk
38—Unau
39—Scorch
40—Biblical pronoun
42—Found on the head
44—Spanish aunt
45—Yield

47—Father of Ajax
49—Longtime actor
50—The zygomatic bone
51—Franciscan mission
52—Kind of shoe
53—Any rustic
55—Automaton
56—The middle
57—Discharges
58—Carnival attractions
61—Hold session
63—Joey, for one
70—Disposition
71—Ireland
72—The choice part
73—Silly ones
74—Affirmatives
75—Apportions
77—London gallery
79—Summer on the Loire
81—Certain gloves (var.)

83—Most precipitous
84—Ordinances
86—Brother of Moses
87—Long d-inks
88—Tangible
89—An astringent
90—Sharp pain
92—An opening
93—Crescent-shaped
94—An ostiole
96—Forest clearings
98—Spews forth
101—An authorizing letter
103—Inner satellite of Uranus
106—Not now
107—German admiral
108—Skin disorder
109—One of — the Fates
112—European country (abbr.)
114—River island
116—Rodent

106

PUZZLE 105

HORIZONTAL

1. Muffins
5. Young boys
9. Neckpieces
13. Siamese coins
17. Kind of grass
18. Essayist
19. Competent
20. Trades
22. Biblical name
23. Height
25. Strong white fiber
26. Dad's helpmate
28. Not big enough
30. Chemical suffix
31. Repeat orisons
32. Nothing
34. Decorated cloak button
35. English cathedral city
36. Gainsay
37. He bore a burden
39. Italian river
41. Sucking fish
44. Declares
46. Take out
50. Name in baseball
51. Decompose
52. Simpleton
54. Plunger
55. Ore pit
56. Biological categories
59. Used for clothing
61. ——, vidi, vici
62. Ancient
63. Devout
65. Feigns
67. Greek goddess
69. Style of car
71. Turn inside out
72. Voiding
75. Traveled alternate route
77. Welsh-English river
80. Pearl Buck heroine
81. Musical prince
83. Astronomical instrument
84. Famous painter
85. Sharp tastes
87. God of love
89. Possesses
90. Festivals
91. Regard
93. Landed properties
96. Doctrinal formulas
97. Quantity of paper
99. Spanish dining halls
100. Recompense
101. Chalice
104. Kind of kick
106. Polish vigorously
107. A divided position
108. Famous general
111. ———horn
114. The smallest state
117. To accumulate
118. Repetition
120. Ancient district of Asia Minor
121. Voided escutcheons
122. Come in second
123. Not there
124. Musical compositions
125. Lodge members
126. Grafted (Her.)
127. Sacred vessels
128. Sins

VERTICAL

1. Street Arab
2. Growing out
3. Haze
4. Boots for horses
5. Room for action
6. Brass, for one
7. Per ——
8. Learned men
9. To cudgel
10. Newspaper item
11. Reserved
12. Spanish matron
13. Appointed
14. To taunt
15. Savor
16. Chip of stone
17. Ashen
21. Weaver's reed
24. Old-womanish
27. Girl's name
29. Nobleman
33. Smear with fat
36. French painter
37. Flowers
38. Pack
40. Hit musical
41. San ——
42. Wicked
43. Beggar
44. First-rate
45. Spill liquid upon
47. Come to pass
48. Mind
49. Sister of Ares
51. Vengeance
53. Bullfighters on foot
56. Tutelar deities
57. Marsh grass
58. Mountain chain
60. A pry
63. Soak
64. London gallery
66. Spread grass
68. The harbor seal
70. Buenas
72. Ballot
73. Exclamation
74. Mr. Vidal
76. Japanese songs
78. Winter vehicle
79. Osculate
82. A sea
84. Legal instrument
86. Some grapes
88. John Wayne, for one
90. Sponger's delight
92. Horse
94. A squama
95. Girl's name
96. Yield
98. Movable
100. Author A.A. and family
101. In addition
102. Liturgical headdress (var.)
103. Coral island
105. Mountaineer's peg
107. Wading bird
108. Solitary one
109. Redacts
110. Unfledged bird
112. A migration
113. Exploit
115. Row
116. Period of time
119. Female ruff

PUZZLE 106

HORIZONTAL

1. A king of the Moabites
6. Lean-to
10. Oklahoma city
14. Catkin
19. Lewis Carroll heroine
20. Not there
21. Word on the Wall
22. Philippine island
23. Famous ship
25. A race track
27. Iowa town
28. Actress and forest
30. Harvest
31. High notes
32. —— Gatos
33. Honor cards
34. Chart
36. Miss Stevens
38. Overhead railways
39. Footless animal
40. Romeo slew him
42. Basketball team
44. Obtained by theft
47. U.S. defense arm
49. Ribbed woolen cloth
53. Organized body
54. American author
55. Early garden
57. Shoestring
58. Matures
59. Plural of beatus
60. Hindu queen
62. Frigg
63. French formal dance
64. Climbing palm
65. "—— Smokey"
67. Issue copiously
68. Letters
69. Amuses
75. Refurbish a lawn
78. Surpass
81. Populated area
82. Enrich
83. American inventor
84. Bark cloth
85. Sign of the zodiac
87. Time long since past
88. Sand hill
89. Lethal
90. Animosity
92. Singing cheerfully
94. —— de Balzac
95. Minor prophet
97. City in Flanders
98. Yearn
99. Burmese demon
102. Angers
104. Soak in
105. Roster
106. Holy Mother Mary (L. abbr.)
109. Desserts
111. Miss Chase
113. High explosive
115. Wild plum
116. Winter visitor
119. California county
121. Russian union
122. Active volcano
123. Kind of eye?
124. Detested
125. Dirty
126. Network
127. Unit of force
128. White poplar

VERTICAL

1. Fundamental
2. Texas shrine
3. Covers the inside
4. Behaves
5. Parrot
6. Participated
7. Droves
8. Lake port
9. Popular singer
10. Printer's measures
11. Close
12. Interior
13. Hold back
14. A king of Judah
15. Shock of hair
16. Mr. Zola
17. Brazilian port
18. Volcanic tuff
24. Georgia city
26. Church parts
29. Hindu garment
33. Imitates
35. English dramatist
37. And others (abbr.)
39. Mountains
40. Flour-and-egg food
41. Kind of auto
43. Rods
44. Sign of healing
45. Loose garment
46. Russian city
47. Menu item
48. Dispatched
50. Medical combining form
51. Lively dance
52. Biblical place
54. Village in Palestine
56. Later portion of the Tertiary
59. Tend a roast
61. Fencing swords
64. Karel Capek play
66. Certain dictionary (abbr.)
67. Classes
69. Greenland settlement
70. Ibsen heroine
71. Taunt
72. Baal
73. Undershot water wheel
74. Puffs up
75. Re-arranged
76. Happening
77. Warbled
78. Roman patriot
79. Armadillo
80. Pallid
84. Sharp flavor
86. Half: a prefix
89. Fountain
91. Order of architecture
93. Blow
94. Old Testament book
96. Retailer, for one
98. Small
99. Jewish month
100. Nest-building fish
101. Portable shelters
103. Ray
105. Bitter chemical substance
106. Roofing material
107. The black nightshade
108. American general
110. Printer's term
112. Relative
114. Defense arm
115. Thick slice
117. Like a brewed liquor
118. Engineer's group (abbr.)
120. Chinese tea

PUZZLE 107

HORIZONTAL

1. Popular singer
5. Bills
10. Statements
15. Penny
19. Aleutian island
20. Sultan's decree
21. White poplar
22. Cry of Bacchanals
23. Slender
24. Bails
25. Certain legumes
26. Delineate
27. Alpine province
29. Camper's need
30. ——— Bede
31. Neck vertebra
32. Moon buggy
34. Sea bird
36. Tall talos
38. Hebrew letter
41. Small child
42. Famous Vincent
44. Turf
45. Spanish article
48. Spirit of hostility
50. Dejection
52. Builder's need
54. Ceremonies
55. Biblical name
56. Mr. Rogers
58. Specific taste
59. Sharif
60. Pewter solder
61. Hue
63. A marine clay
64. Communications
66. Bar offering
67. Hoped for
69. Comfortable
70. Protective cloth
71. Half: a prefix
72. Student monitor
76. Drone
77. Feigns illness
82. Solitary
83. Lukewarm
85. Printer's mark
86. Olive genus
87. Famous violin
89. Tribe of Israel
90. Fragment
91. Attract
92. Panders
94. Clergyman's salary
96. Religious festival
97. Chemical suffix
98. Poet's word
100. Marsh bird
101. Storage compartment
102. Poet's word
103. Trap
105. Thoroughfares (abbr.)
106. High, today
108. Hurried
111. Jai ———
113. Sea bird
115. Greenland settlement
119. Avouch
120. Utilizing
121. Man's name
123. American inventor
124. Miss Teasdale
125. Style of car
126. Laughing
127. Apartments?
128. Contend in a game
129. Girl's name
130. Dinner course
131. Sabot

VERTICAL

1. Play's personnel
2. Gudrun's husband
3. Agitate
4. Mood
5. Wire measure
6. Declaimed
7. Troubleshooting author
8. TV's Barbara
9. Recent past
10. Poise
11. In the same place (abbr.)
12. American general
13. Large ruminants
14. French pronoun
15. Primitive chisels
16. Wicked
17. Gangrenous stomatitis
18. Bills
28. Water plant
31. Mountain chain
33. Duct
35. Skating area
37. Fabulous bird
38. Italian playing card
39. Soft copal
40. Essential
42. Tropical plants
43. Biblical name
45. A pry
46. Positive terminal
47. Famous violin (short.)
49. Simple
50. Mr. Davis
51. The sun
53. One of a gardener caste
55. Vaunted
57. Warbled
60. Treatise
61. Young lion
62. Pay the bill
65. Command to a horse
66. Edge
68. Biblical wilderness
70. Sign of spring
71. Ventured
72. ——— d'armes
73. Style of type
74. Growing out
75. Festival
76. Insinuations
77. French river
78. Pierce with horns
79. Girl's name
80. French security
81. French author
84. Dance step
85. European starlings
88. Light sarcasm
90. Roasting pin
91. French psychologist
93. Health resort
95. Insignia (sing.)
96. Mend
99. Expunged
101. A fruit
103. Wander
104. Ignore
106. A test
107. Looks for bargains
108. Door fastener
109. Grandparental
110. Antitoxins
112. Analgous (abbr.)
114. Charles Lamb
116. Western state
117. Italian resort
118. Being
120. Home of the brave (abbr.)
122. Theological degree

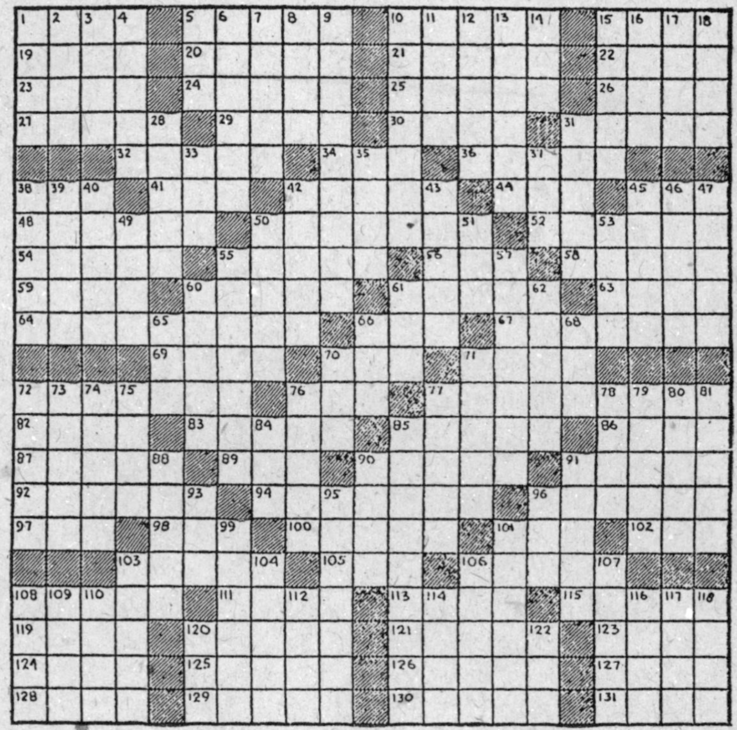
1 2 3 4 5 6 7 8 9 10 11 12 13 14 15 16 17 18
19 20 21 22
23 24 25 26
27 28 29 30 31
32 33 34 35 36 37
38 39 40 41 42 43 44 45 46 47
48 49 50 51 52 53
54 55 56 57 58
59 60 61 62 63
64 65 66 67 68
69 70 71
72 73 74 75 76 77 78 79 80 81
82 83 84 85 86
87 88 89 90 91
92 93 94 95 96
97 98 99 100 101 102
103 104 105 106 107
108 109 110 111 112 113 114 115 116 117 118
119 120 121 122 123
124 125 126 127
128 129 130 131

PUZZLE 108

HORIZONTAL

1. Girl's nickname
6. A tax
10. Ancient Ptolemais
14. Panama province
19. Worship
20. Small pet dog (short.)
21. Accomplishes
22. Kind of orange
23. Occasions
24. Persia
25. Chalices
26. Useful
27. Concerning
28. Famous sleeper
29. Entertain
30. More fastidious
31. Contriving
34. Musical composition
36. Donkey
39. Network
40. Mr. Hunter
42. Granular snow
43. African Negro
46. Perfumed ointments
48. Shoot prepared for grafting
50. One hostile to the Crusaders
52. Spanish writer
53. Cut deeper (Engraving)
55. Tags
56. Kind of race
57. Observed
58. Farm animals
60. A short story
61. Italian commune
62. A fruit
63. Perry's Della
65. One who professes an ism
66. Asiatic kingdom
68. Obliterate
70. Patriotic org.
73. A present to a guest
76. The youngest son
78. Popular singer
82. Brittle
84. Bristle
85. Alodium
86. Musical instrument
87. Ransom
89. Spanish gentlemen
91. Imposing entrance
92. Made irate
94. Lesions
95. Choral composition
96. Cinema "Lil"
97. Detail
99. A cape (Geog.)
100. A child
101. The law thing
102. Abounded
104. Catherine, et al.
107. Treat with contempt
110. Appearing eaten
112. Aries
113. Senseless
117. Long blouse
118. Ceramic square
119. Undulate
120. Roman and pug
121. Ammonia compound
122. Grafted (Her.)
123. European river
124. American Indians
125. A governor of Virginia
126. A sea
127. American author
128. English author

VERTICAL

1. Facts
2. War god
3. Large book
4. General tenor
5. The recent past
6. Specters
7. A color
8. Giraffe-like mammal
9. Decimal base
10. Man in Genesis
11. God of mirth
12. Intellect
13. Ancient ascetics
14. Nullifies
15. Ancient port of Rome
16. Secular
17. To eye
18. Poet's word
29. Once more
32. Little (Isle of Man)
33. —— Creed
35. Grand-parental
36. Armadillo
37. Shoe parts
38. Edible fish
41. Observes
43. Ancient tribe of Britons
44. Dress accessories
45. Beginning
47. With might
48. Blind
49. Salamander
51. Turku
53. Answers
54. Altar screen
57. Crosses over
59. Biblical name
62. Simian
64. Devour
67. Feels
69. President of Germany
70. Get lost!
71. Sports area
72. Range of hills
74. Indians
75. Estate of a lord
76. Touch gently
77. Pub specialties
79. Place of sacrifice
80. Gladden
81. French author and family
83. Bishopric
86. Commercial receptacle
88. Apportion
90. Declaim
91. Unpleasant sensation
93. Greek goddess
95. A she-monster
98. Hardy breed of sheep
100. Cowardly
102. Three-fold
103. Simpletons
105. Plowed land
106. Night sound
107. Kind of party
108. The cougar
109. Distinct part
111. Observes
114. —— Minor
115. Require
116. Being
119. Married

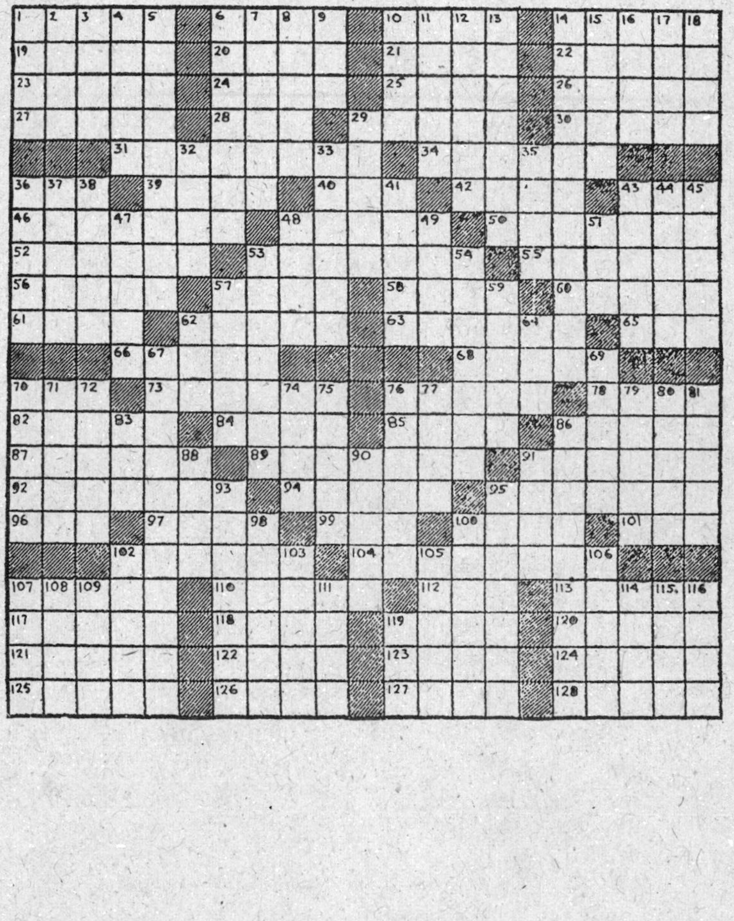

PUZZLE 109

HORIZONTAL

1. Treat's companion
6. Halloween vehicle
11. Pronoun
16. Actress Claire
17. Singer Frankie
18. Novelist Jane
20. Personal
21. Entertainer Steve
22. Joyous
24. Uncouth
25. Suit bid at bridge
27. Wild ox
29. Dumb
30. ——— de boue
31. Is situated
32. Strong blow
33. High note
34. Warbled
36. Weights, in India
37. Muddles
39. Islands, in France
40. Access
42. Inner satellite of Uranus
43. Pure
45. Western state
46. The thigh bone
47. Mexican card game
48. Strong-scented herb
51. Straw broom
52. Offered for consideration
56. Fictional Butler
57. A privilege
58. Chinese liangs
59. Hebrew priest
60. Years (dial.)
61. Dried orchid tubers
62. French composer
63. Profit
64. Salutation
65. Jewish festival
66. Cupolas
67. French aunt
68. Certain performances
70. Black and blue
71. Elapsed
72. Clement
73. Large ruminant
74. Military life
75. A set formula
78. Stupid blunder
79. Fashion fad
83. Literary collections
84. Has terror of
86. Famous river
87. Lively dance
88. Dancer's cymbals
89. College course
90. Heraldic figure
91. Compass reading
92. Large birds
94. Force
95. Bridal paths
97. Diminutive suffix
98. Arabs
100. Genus of mosquitoes
102. Site of the Round Table
104. Esculent vegetable
105. Angry
106. Plowman
107. Massenet opera
108. Hungarian composer
109. Kills

VERTICAL

1. Three-pronged spear
2. Frenchman's dream
3. The yellow bugle
4. Small beds
5. Jewish ravioli
6. Reckless fellows
7. Chest sounds
8. Certain paintings
9. Undivided
10. Greek comic dramatist
11. Hindu poet
12. Graceful dance
13. Compass reading
14. Newspaper paragraph
15. Fills the gas tank
16. American President
19. Stone of a drupe
20. Leek-green quartz
23. Legal document
26. French river
28. Little ———
32. Opprobrium
35. Guttural sounds
36. Fastener
37. Protective covering
38. Skew surface (Geom.)
39. Perfidious one
41. "Let's get ———!"
42. Fabulist
44. School dances
46. Pyrexia
47. Liberates
48. Served with coffee
49. Biblical place
50. Dogma
51. Bundles
52. Covered with macadam
53. O'Casey, et al.
54. The choice part
55. Ate
57. Declined
58. Oldest Dravidian language
61. Blinded
62. Fido's friend
63. One of the Three Kings of Cologne
65. Clip suddenly
66. Coins
67. Ram down
69. Wurttemberg measures
70. Disembarks
71. Liver paste
73. Part of a man's suit
74. Gathers
75. Appraises
76. Kind of paint
77. Peace pipe
78. Swiss canton
79. Land elevation
80. Cuddles
81. A witness (rare)
82. Weather word
85. Elevates
86. Former Egyptian VIP
90. Michelangelo work
93. Deep, prolonged breath
94. Half: a prefix
95. Biblical name
96. Travel by water
97. Wriggling
99. Philippine tree (var.)
101. Before
103. A language group (abbr.)

116

PUZZLE 110

HORIZONTAL

1. —— Raton
5. Curtain fabric
10. Ultimate
15. A tax
19. Baal, for one
20. Attendant on a lord
21. Worship
22. Ripped
23. Executive rap
25. Expression of sympathy
27. Bitter vetch
28. Roster
29. Toddler
31. First-rate
32. Headwear
33. Snares
35. Mountaineer's peg
37. Wash lightly
39. Scold
41. Regulate
43. Repeated tiresomely
46. Lessen
47. Long tooth
48. British gun
50. Name in the news
51. Peau de ——
52. Body of water
53. The dill
55. Father, in Paris
56. Tourist haven
57. Horny substance
59. Defies
61. Inlet
62. Bladder-like
64. Arouse to action
66. Overlooked
68. Massachusetts cape
69. River, in Spain
70. Sailor
71. Revokes
75. Spanish title
77. Caesar crossed it
81. Japanese statesman
82. Longs
84. Puts off
86. Egg: comb. form
87. Gasp
89. Famous Martha
90. Rational
91. Comfortable
92. Go in
94. Peruse
96. Early Persian
97. Ransack
98. Secured
100. Expands
102. Scorcher
103. Mother-of-pearl
105. Kind of Persian rug
106. Husk: comb. form
107. Honor card
109. Chinese secret society
111. Mountain on Crete
112. Eldest: law
113. Compass reading
116. Certain speech sounds
119. Implies secondarily (obs.)
122. Fixed routine
123. Public warehouse
124. Measure of capacity
125. Meadows
126. Lohengrin's bride
127. Scottish chemist
128. Girl's name
129. Vain

VERTICAL

1. Color of azurite
2. Scent
3. Compels
4. Man's nickname
5. Band of color
6. Game of skill
7. Rave
8. Business abbr.
9. Encountering
10. Constituents
11. Artificial language
12. One of the Fates
13. Warmth
14. Man's name
15. Sainte (abbr.)
16. Contesters
17. Killer whale
18. Abound
24. Gladden
26. Russian Soviet leader
30. Baseball name
34. Appraise
35. Muse
36. Public officer
38. Fastener
39. Fundamental
40. Valuable wood
41. A staff
42. Russian river
44. Uncanny
45. Great fear
47. Pen for sheep
49. Firn
52. Stern fast, for one
54. A woven fabric
57. Beautiful
58. Nostrils
59. Kind of money?
60. Signs of healing
63. Chinese pagoda
65. —— Yutang
67. Swiss canton
71. Mature
72. Babylonian hero
73. North and South America
74. European coal region
75. Chides (dial.)
76. Genus of Old World herbs
77. Man's name
78. Faced
79. Immature seed
80. African river
83. Gypsy gentlemen
85. Popular crazes
88. A tissue
91. Thailand
93. Right-hand page
95. Famous author
96. To shackle
97. Satisfied again
99. Hummed
101. Football player
102. Spanish matron
104. Growing out
106. Kind of writing paper
107. Land measure
108. How to play it
110. Bite with effort
112. Poker stake
114. Man's name
115. Being
117. Ross, for one
118. Traveler's assoc.
120. Painter's need
121. Fourth caliph

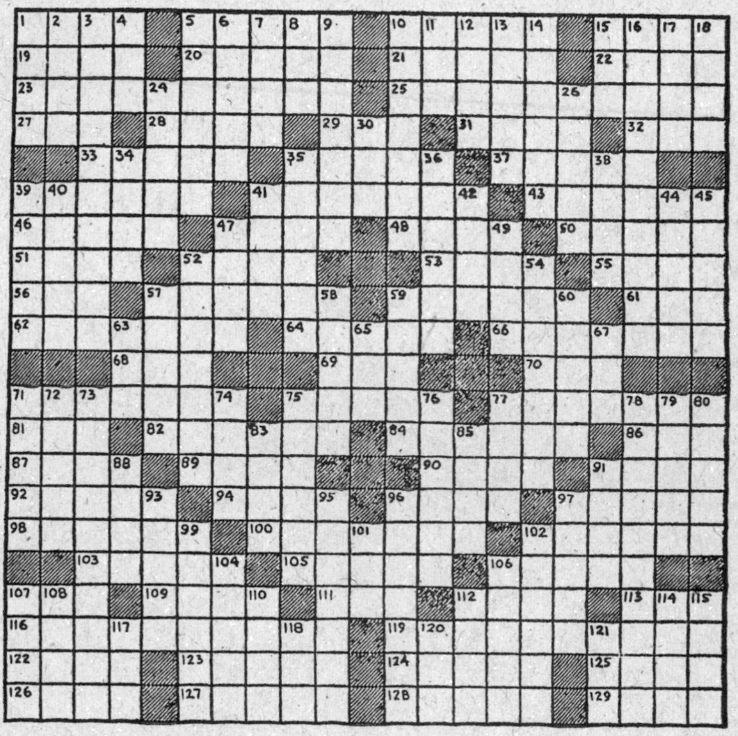

PUZZLE 111

HORIZONTAL

1. Herds of whales
5. Island off Venezuela
10. Polynesian island group
15. To mince
19. Mormon state
20. California county
21. Not fancy
22. Broadtopped hill
23. Italian commune
24. Correct
25. Menu items
26. Portent
27. Hawaiian volcano
29. Iranian (and): comb. form
31. Vacillates
33. Emerald Isle
34. Greek island
35. Withered
36. California county
39. Footwear
40. Accented
44. God of mirth
45. Mountain lakes
46. Biblical weeds
47. Corrida cheer
48. Upon
49. Rail birds
50. Dinner course
51. A dye
52. Honey
53. Hip joint in cattle
54. Social gathering
55. Plowed land
56. Enjoyment
58. Greek island
59. English county
60. Caresses
61. Actor Robert
62. Icelandic tale
63. Candles
66. More rational
67. Hated
71. Scents
72. Demon
73. Biblical name
74. Salutation
75. Cuts down
76. Purposive
77. Part of a mortise
78. Iowa town
79. Farm animal
80. Tropical trees
81. Famous for its cliffs
82. Move furtively
83. Italian island
85. Theater boxes
86. Silvery fishes
87. Pilaster
88. More wise
89. Pack
90. Store in a granary
93. Choral composition
94. Pardons
98. Amalekite king
99. Combine
101. Mohammedan nymph
103. Poet's valley
104. Certain
105. Son of Zeus and Europa
106. Blundered
107. Being
108. Equal
109. Marsh bird
110. Civet
111. Leading man

VERTICAL

1. Island of the Marianas
2. Wheaten flour
3. Suffix for Japanese ship names
4. Polishes
5. Famous aviatrix
6. Actor Novarro
7. Carbamide
8. Storage compartment
9. Firedogs
10. European herrings
11. Unaccompanied
12. Hawaiian loincloth
13. A fuel
14. Replied
15. Cooks use them
16. No place like it
17. Hebrew measure
18. Cookware
28. Skills
30. Soaks
32. War god
34. Colorful sea
35. Wander
36. Rascal
37. Traveler's haven
38. Soap plant
39. Vermont city
40. Sailors
41. Ship's protective device
42. Ignore
43. Put off
45. Some are guided
46. Italian playing card
49. Closes
50. Philippine island
51. A tapestry
53. Peter and Nicholas
54. The whole jury
55. Carpenter's tool
57. Imitators
58. Of sound waves
59. A fabric
61. Bette
62. Spanish title
63. Weighty volumes
64. Abyssinian town (var.)
65. Might
66. Alabama city
67. Sand hills
68. Dravidian language
69. Happening
70. Office items
72. Girl's name
73. Cut
76. Fits of ill humor
77. Old song hit
78. Fishes of the herring family
80. A tree
81. Venetian magistrate
82. Curse of cities
84. Peril
85. Newest
86. To straddle
88. Yuccalike plant
89. Open lesions
90. Pant
91. Chills and fever
92. Unusual
93. Skirt length
94. Mink and sable
95. Huge
96. Lohengrin's bride
97. Prophet
100. Insect egg
102. Money of account

PUZZLE 112

HORIZONTAL

1. Smart
5. Disgrace
10. Romeo slew him
15. Certain bills
19. Leading man
20. Corn breads
21. Love, in Rome
22. Western state
23. Popular novelist
24. Sluggish
25. Delaware, for one
26. Legendary king of Rome
27. French musician
29. Artificial language
31. Activities
33. European river
34. Pleasant expression
36. Man in Genesis
37. Kind of soup
40. Plant organs
42. Testator's concern
46. Zodiac sign
47. Petty malice
48. Spread grass
50. Leaf of the calyx
51. Goad
52. American author
53. Dinner course
55. Invalid
56. Weep
57. Depict
58. Aida's lover
60. The turmeric
61. Football team
63. Jewish festival
65. Needlers
67. Pertaining to India: comb. form
69. Preclude
71. Black and Red
72. The tunny
76. Clio, et al.
78. Affirm
82. Any split pulse
83. Dutch scholar
85. Silly one
87. Cut down
88. Armadillo
90. Place of sacrifice
91. Racer, for one
92. Skirt length
93. Buffoons
95. Conger
96. Nest-building fish
97. Spanish dining halls
98. Moves furtively
100. Typist's needs
102. Go back
103. A fruit
105. English navigator
106. Simple
107. Ship area
111. Discussion, today
112. Large waterfall
116. Table spread
117. Italian river
119. Likeness
121. Dies —
122. Blast
123. French school
124. American composer
125. Certificate (abbr.)
126. Bugle call
127. American poet
128. Coated with icing
129. Cabbage plant

VERTICAL

1. Pal
2. Queen of heaven
3. Rainbow
4. Pampered
5. Hard mineral
6. Sharpener
7. The dill
8. Sea (Fr.)
9. Make assessment
10. Word of promise
11. Pierre's friend
12. Wander
13. Greek goddess
14. Unruffled
15. Chemical element
16. Toiletry case
17. Title
18. Shinto temples
28. Shield
30. Coin
32. A sea
34. Restricted
35. Inward
37. Slip
38. Actor Flynn
39. She wept for her children
40. Whirls
41. Word in the Psalms
43. River in Venezuela
44. German silver coin
45. Raines and Fitzgerald
47. Cebine monkey
49. Titled women
52. Mythical Greek woman
53. Teasdale, et al.
54. Death
57. Peter's
58. Form of riddle
59. Ray
62. By way of
64. Take exception
66. D-Day vessel (abbr.)
68. Papal veil
70. Reigning
72. U.S. President
73. Kind of fur
74. To censure
75. Animal fat
77. Flies aloft
79. Author Zola
80. Underwater detecting device
81. Kind of dance
84. Acid in apples
86. Turkish measure
89. They deal in land
91. Beating other reporters
92. Motherless calf
94. Sports equipment
96. Mr. Eban
97. Antitoxins
99. Strikes
101. Sterile
102. White crystalline hydrocarbon
104. Decree
106. Necromancy
107. Mail
108. Genus of olives
109. Harvest
110. Central American tree
112. Vena —
113. Scope
114. Man's name
115. Head (Fr.)
118. Hebrew priest
120. Honey

122

PUZZLE 113

HORIZONTAL

1. Sloping roadways
6. Crushing snake
11. Degrees
16. Hindu poet
17. Burdened
18. Benevolent
20. Ardent partisan
21. Pea tree
22. Beasts
24. Cuckoo
25. Animal fats
27. Entertainer
29. Novel by Rudyard Kipling
30. Dwarf
32. Tapered piece of metal
33. Skills
34. Verdi opera
35. Corners
37. Lake port
39. Large volcano
40. Smile with scorn
41. Six-line stanza
43. Ancient ascetics
45. Ardent desire
46. A drove
48. Peter and Ivan
49. Novelist Vicki
50. Corrects
54. W.W. II theater
55. —— Bill
59. Scent
60. Pungent bulb
62. Tibetan city
64. San —— Obispo
65. Roman bronze
66. Three: a prefix
67. Bitter vetch
68. M.D.'s aides
69. Pintail duck
71. Poet Eugene
73. Dress feathers
75. Hosea, in the New Testament
76. Most sapid
78. The turmeric
80. Bar offerings
82. Countenance
83. Rounded ornament
85. Move swiftly
86. Dormant
89. Instruments like guillotines
91. Overacted
95. Zodiac sign
96. Henry or Edsel
97. Uttered
99. Vermont city
100. Bugle call
101. Presently
102. Girl's name
104. Titled woman
105. Consumed
106. City's nominal ancestor
108. Madagascan mammal
110. Energy
111. Restoration
113. Derived from gold
115. Football teams
117. Harsh
118. Headed bolt
119. Girl's name
120. Ventured
121. Slag
122. Muscles

VERTICAL

1. Deep gorges
2. Past
3. Small particle
4. Iron
5. Soak in liquid
6. Scaremonger
7. Sacks
8. Harem room
9. Girl's name
10. Enlivens
11. Kind of daisy
12. Melodies
13. Arabian chieftain
14. Knave of clubs
15. More sinuous
16. Right of holding
19. Ignores
20. Pub game
23. Sting
26. Ireland
28. Footed vases
31. Leash, for one
34. Not vegetable or mineral
36. Germ
38. Prussian city
39. To record (var.)
40. To eschew
42. Musical group
44. Devour
45. Ancient Irish capital
47. Professional man
49. Certain hounds
50. Menu item
51. Dropsy
52. Aaron's brother
53. Rumanian river
55. Reveals
56. Imprecation
57. Ocean vessel
58. Letters
61. Fuel
63. Pronoun
70. Public warehouses
71. Nourish
72. Officer of the gorsedd
73. Blanches
74. French resort
75. The number eight
77. Wading bird
79. Old times (archaic)
81. Insensible
83. Farm area
84. Literary gleanings
86. One of a Turkic horde
87. Declaims
88. Matured
89. New frontier
90. Zion
92. Makes a journey
93. Valuable fur
94. Supposes
96. Duped
98. Manage
101. Lean
103. Word in the Psalms
106. Pitcher
107. Scottish poet
108. Evens the score
109. Wax
112. Girl's name
114. A British Order (abbr.)
116. Solemn promise

PUZZLE 114

HORIZONTAL

1. Weakens
5. Crazy
9. Rubber trees
13. Misfortunes
17. Dogma
18. Neglect
19. Girl's name
20. Relative
22. Rose essence
23. They supply cities
25. Lethargic sleep
26. The Nina, for one
28. Fore-and-aft rigged vessels
30. Dry
31. Old musical hit
32. Manipulate fraudulently
34. River duck
35. Female ruff
36. Monster
37. Serfs
39. Degree
41. Garland
44. Regards
46. Light meals
50. Less colorful
51. Danish county
52. Install in office
54. Mohawk, for one
55. Takes a chair
56. Garment folds
59. Ireland
61. Slay (dial.)
62. Hebrew priest
63. Primitive
65. Opposed to starboard
67. Girl's name
69. Oleoresin
71. Article of food
72. Strong cotton cloth
75. Large woody plants
77. Noun suffix
80. Certain Latvian native
81. Large volume
83. Optical masers
84. Chapter of the Koran
85. Arabian chieftain (var.)
87. "Rio——"
89. Overhead railways
90. Cougars
91. To impair
93. Remembers
96. A cotton crepe
97. Chinese liang
99. Fine line of a letter
100. Garment
101. Milkfish
104. Creese (var.)
106. Fictional dog hero
107. Hailing term (Naut.)
108. Longshoremen's org.
111. Book by Charles Dickens
114. Piratical vessels (Hist.)
117. Prefix for naut or dome
118. Hudson River sight
120. Goddess of peace
121. Guide
122. Ardor
123. Monthly bill
124. Girl's name
125. Ancient country
126. Attica township
127. A kind of wood
128. Grafted (Her.)

VERTICAL

1. Bristles
2. A merry-andrew
3. Resound
4. Part-time correspondent
5. To squint
6. Biblical name
7. Lillian or Dorothy
8. Wanting drink
9. Eskimo knife
10. Deprivation
11. Choose
12. Obis
13. Grossly disrespectful
14. Wild animal
15. Biblical outcast
16. Tally
17. Russian agency
21. Scottish Gaelic
24. Think
27. Standard
29. Cereal grains
33. Turns to the off side
36. Poems
37. Testator's concern
38. Pintail duck
40. Clergyman
41. Church part
42. Fasten
43. Aneroid barometer
44. Uncles (dial.)
45. To yacht
47. Showy plants
48. Large vat
49. Winter vehicle
51. One who transfers property
53. English chemist
56. Use block letters
57. A roofing material
58. Short fishing line
60. American Indians
63. Not an amateur
64. Jane Austen novel
66. College degree (abbr.)
68. Bear witness to
70. Pronoun
72. Corner of square sail
73. San——
74. Arabian chieftain
76. Electrical units
78. Ages
79. Level to the ground
82. French summers
84. Become
86. Lab containers
88. Maple genus
90. Time for diversion
92. St. Philip
94. Semites
95. Collection of books
96. The mastwood
98. Proceeded with difficulty
100. Pure
101. Exclamations
102. Dissipate
103. Russian union
105. Name in the news
107. Deputy
108. Lifeless
109. Slowly (L.)
110. On the ocean
112. Three (Ger.)
113. Bang
115. Notion
116. Persia
119. Suffix in adjectives

PUZZLE 115

HORIZONTAL

1. Mimicked
5. Henry, for one
10. Resinous substance
15. A phial
19. Wine and —
20. Open Eskimo boat
21. Papal veil
22. Vain
23. Dye indigo
24. French security
25. American composer
26. Channel
27. Word before Hat or man
29. Bank abbr.
31. Acts of avoidance
33. Price
34. Explosive sound
36. Epic poetry
37. Chemical element
40. Dirtier
42. Builds
46. Girl's name
47. Mountain pass
48. — Frome
50. Nest-building fish
51. — die (L.)
52. Hair-care item
54. Uncanny
56. Musical group
57. Drive slantingly
58. Bundles
60. To reach (dial.)
62. — Hunter
63. Enrapture
65. Clayey
67. Lowly
69. English dean
70. Bird
71. Fly aloft
72. Love apple
75. Fastening pin
76. Old maid
80. A wing
81. Biblical city
83. Grating
85. South American city
86. Capital of Latvia
88. A game at dice
90. Loud, ringing sound
91. Ancient Greek coin
92. Oust
94. Affray
96. Govt. service
97. Anoint (archaic)
98. Mathematical instrument
100. Fountain dishes
102. Gazes
103. The holm oak
105. Spanish title
106. Letters
107. Common soldiers
111. Deface
112. Plot together
116. Indian
117. Growing out
119. Sea birds
121. Render turbid
122. Hop kiln
123. Actor — Lloyd
124. Winged
125. Active volcano
126. City in New York
127. — nous
128. Lay in surrounding matter
129. American engineer

VERTICAL

1. Man in Genesis
2. Tree
3. City in Oklahoma
4. Frail
5. One versed in the law
6. Catkin
7. Follows eta or jas
8. Consume
9. Quantities of yarn
10. Penitent
11. Native metal
12. Surface a road
13. Not inert
14. Delaware Indian
15. Dissect alive
16. Idea: comb. form
17. Icelandic measure
18. Camera part
28. Genus of African trees
30. Observe
32. Rail bird
34. Mud volcano
35. Persian city
37. Hereditary Hindu class
38. Pungent bulb
39. French psychologist
40. For the —
41. More unusual
43. Cariban Indian
44. A cross
45. French river
47. Daughter of Helios
49. Insect egg
52. Burmese seaport
53. A crossette (Arch.)
55. Reverberating
58. Gasps
59. Staid
61. — Ti, legendary Chinese emperor
64. Narrow inlet
66. Fragrant blossom
68. Abbr. on envelope
70. Twin of Remus
71. Whirls
72. Biblical weeds
73. Cocktail garnish
74. Conjuration
75. Pigeons
76. Boxes
77. River in Italy
78. French school
79. Chest sounds
82. Portuguese title
84. More cunning
87. Nimbleness
89. Words on the Wall
91. He's — (a bender)
93. Biblical name
95. Miss Ferber
97. The sweetsop
99. A hydrocarbon
101. Large arteries
102. Felt intuitively
104. Gaseous element
106. A short story
107. Unit of illumination
108. Bellow
109. — facto
110. To season
112. Crustacean
113. Greek letter
114. Fruit peel
115. High notes
118. Sailor
120. A tree

PUZZLE 116

HORIZONTAL

1. City in New York
5. City in Illinois
10. English author
15. Town in Arizona
19. Cowboy gear
20. A love intrigue
21. City in Illinois
22. Emerald Isle
23. Mohammedan priest
24. Choral composition
25. Slant
26. Dregs
27. Volcano on Martinique
29. Headstrong
30. Stringed instrument
31. Anoint (archaic)
32. Michigan city
34. Wood sorrel
36. Mother of the Graces
38. Aries
41. Speck
42. Take as one's own
44. Dull routine
45. Keg (dial.)
48. Ammonia compounds
50. Gretna Green visitors
52. Alabama city
54. Hue
55. A substitute
56. Exclamation
58. Makes void
59. Ancient country
60. Flower
61. Rascal
63. Narrow inlets
64. Turncoats
66. Small bed
67. American Indian
69. Burden
70. Chart
71. A shred
72. Language of Jesus
76. School dance
77. Climatic conditions (obs.)
82. Capture
83. English navigator
85. List of candidates
86. English river
87. Tapestry
89. Chinese dynasty
90. Babylonian hero
91. Biblical name
92. New Jersey borough
94. Pennsylvania city
96. Six-line stanza
97. Poet's word
98. Xenon
100. Whirls
101. Wooden peg
102. Compass reading
103. Coins in the fountain
105. Girl of song
106. A red dye
108. Name in baseball
111. California city
113. Gudrun's husband
115. Poe's bird
119. Biblical weed
120. Odin, Thor, Tyr et al.
121. Rancid bacon
123. Basis of pol
124. Greek mountain
125. Division of a drama
126. Man's name
127. Soon
128. Require
129. Atelier need
130. Ignore
131. —— majesty

VERTICAL

1. Journey
2. City in New York
3. Gem stone
4. Arabian country
5. Machine part
6. Love token
7. Greek letters
8. Regrets
9. Opposed to heresy
10. Form again
11. Girl's name
12. Greek market place
13. Big or Little
14. Compass reading
15. Middle
16. Great Lake port
17. Window part
18. Poker stake
28. Sea duck
31. Illinois city
33. —— Angeles
35. Imitate
37. Often chewed
38. The blacksnake
39. Soap plant
40. Italian city
42. At —— for words
43. Treatise
45. Eyelashes
46. Moslem god
47. Plaster of Paris
49. City in Alaska
50. Sea eagles
51. The urial
53. Eruct
55. Kentucky city
57. Genus of agarics
60. Unreasoning fear
61. To soak
62. The first part
65. District of India
66. Surpass
68. South American river
70. Bon ——
71. Popular cant
72. —— of Two Cities
73. Peep show
74. Ohio city
75. Intend
76. Sharpens
77. Septs
78. Scotch caps
79. Conserve of grapes
80. Flowers
81. Growing out
84. Obstacle
85. A sting ray
88. Mourns over
90. Miss Adams
91. God of the sea
93. Swiss river
95. Attire
96. Relative of Mayday
99. Lake in New York
101. Spread by rumor
103. Walk
104. Alleviates
106. Oleoresin
107. Brazilian seaport
108. English school
109. Ornamental container
110. Scottish Gaelic
112. A tree
114. Narrate
116. Weathercock
117. Love god
118. Not any
120. Peer Gynt's mother
122. Prefix to Cornish names

ACROSS

1 A rebuff
5 Broadway musical
10 Broadway musical
15 Broadway musical
19 Star of "Uncle Vanya"
20 Immature (colloq.)
21 Canopy of heaven
22 River in France
23 Swan genus
24 Love feast
25 Disease of rye
26 The Wise Men
27 Musical for Alexis Smith
29 Malay gibbon
31 Snuffled
33 Slave and carpenter
34 Patron saint of France
36 Dye indigo
37 Broadway comedy hit
40 Jerusalem thorns
42 Broadway musical
46 Jackets and collars
47 Source of Eve
48 Wooden shoe
50 Colorado resort
51 Marbles
52 Spurious
54 Biblical name
56 Author: George —

57 One (Fr. fem.)
58 Developed, as oranges
60 River of Hades
62 Scotch society (abbr.)
63 Conferred with enemy
65 To angle in
67 Gladdened
69 Sea birds
70 Flora and fauna
71 Straw beehive
72 " — Out"
75 Madness
76 A lung inflammation
80 Early auto
81 Animal of Madagascar
83 Neptune's spear
85 Bank abbr.
86 Greek temple
88 Leveled to the ground
90 " — Abe Lincoln"
91 Facts
92 Heating vessels
94 Kitchen gadget
96 Husing or Sorensen
97 Actress: Marta —
98 Broadway musical
100 Bismarck, for one
102 Approaching
103 Quick, sharp sound

105 Choir plums
106 Swiss canton
107 Terminated
111 The turmeric
112 Star of "Deathtrap"
116 Heroic in scale
117 " — of a City"
119 Belle —
121 Church part
122 Pack of cards
123 The choice part
124 Pacific archipelago
125 Ascend
126 Bishoprics
127 Girl's name (Fr.)
128 Dutch painter
129 " — Charles"

DOWN

1 "Bus — "
2 Recline lazily
3 Celebes ox
4 Has reference
5 Indo-European language
6 Hot wine drink
7 Distrained (Early English Law)
8 British labor party (abbr.)
9 Grommet
10 " — in His Humour"
11 Former political union (abbr.)
12 Electronic insects?
13 Actress Massey
14 Ruth —, of the "Ziefeld Follies"

15 Wanderers, sometimes
16 Inland sea
17 He wrote "Picnic"
18 Irish novelist
28 Hostelries
30 Duck genus
32 Bantu tribe
34 Social presentation
35 Genus of worms
37 General structure (colloq.)
38 Babylonian hero
39 Gardener's need
40 Stiff
41 Bridge star
43 Aside
44 Sight or smell
45 Concluded
47 Rakes
49 Make lace edging
52 Star of 55 Down
53 To begin
55 " — and I"
58 Wild
59 A right (L.)
61 Choose
64 Space vehicle
66 Eared seal
68 Himalayan mountain
70 Small casks (Naut.)
71 Exhaust
72 Cockney's wasp

73 " — of a Salesman"
74 "Lorna —"
75 "Sound of — "
76 Biblical name
77 Coronet
78 Bury
79 Endure
82 Deface
84 Greek letters
87 Certain bills (slang)
89 One to be exiled
91 Dejected
93 Window part
95 To anger
97 Actor: Rip —
99 Stringed instrument
101 Drinks to
102 Capital of Iran
104 English dramatist
106 Star of "Comedy in Music"
107 Cincinnati team
108 Fencing sword
109 Indian groom (var.)
110 In Rangoon, a measure
112 " — Eyre"
113 English painter
114 Greek mountain
115 Graceful animal
118 Abbr. on roadmap
120 Toddler

PUZZLE 118

HORIZONTAL

1. Rich fabrics
6. Road sign
10. Small particle
14. Imitating
19. Roman magistrate
20. Roof edge
21. East Indian herb
22. Underwater detecting device
23. Form of aircraft
25. Form of motorboat
27. Exclamation
28. Commences
30. Ego
31. Noun suffix
32. Operated
33. Breakwater
34. Bombycid moth
36. A Berber
38. Poet's word
39. Food regimen
40. A buffoon
42. Chemical element
44. Superficial show
47. Conjectured
49. Primer
53. Alter
54. Farm structure
55. Japanese porgies
57. Stone slab (var.)
58. Split
59. Acid in apples
60. Serfs
62. Egyptian god (var.)
63. Constellation
64. Buckingham, for one
65. Reschooling
67. Amazon estuary
68. Aspect (obs.)
69. Colossal
75. Abet
78. Headwear
81. Sacred image (var.)
82. Drama unit
83. English author
84. Philippine vine
85. One of the Mets
87. Concludes
88. Weathercock
89. Besom, for one
90. Most rational
92. Hunting dogs
94. Large, heavy hammer
95. Platform
97. Blasts
98. Large, flat-bottomed boat
99. Sack
102. Forearm bone
104. The law thing
105. Pack
106. Food for infants
109. Macaws
111. Yeans (dial.)
113. English surgeon
115. Wheel hub
116. The Nautilus, et al.
119. The Titanic
121. Biblical name
122. Entice
123. Standard
124. Concerning
125. Bowling alleys
126. Kind of salad
127. Saintes (abbr.)
128. Word in the Psalms

VERTICAL

1. Noted composer
2. Girl's name
3. Italian city
4. Ancient country
5. Dry
6. Set of seven objects
7. One of a Turkic horde
8. Above
9. Relevancy
10. A tree
11. Tops, etc.
12. More mature
13. Game fish
14. Viper
15. North or South
16. Senseless
17. John — Garner
18. Best-selling author
24. Willow
26. Bid
29. Drunkards
33. Variegated
35. Member of the family
37. Enemies
39. Low sand hill
40. Derived from gold
41. Stop
43. Swimming
44. Mexican measure
45. Arabian chieftain
46. Russian river
47. Festive
48. Force
50. Half: a prefix
51. Biblical name
52. Sounded vibrantly
54. Poise
56. Slavish
59. Female horses
61. Fry lightly
64. Knave of clubs
66. French island
67. Kicked a football
69. Russian planes
70. Soup ingredient
71. Midday
72. Certain bills
73. Mountain chain
74. Man's name
75. Reversals of position
76. Approaches
77. Containers
78. English poet
79. Excited
80. Large book
84. Expanded
86. Son of Isaac
89. To bloe
91. Lodge doorkeeper
93. Liang of China
94. To despise
96. Gastropod mollus
98. Prepar clams
99. Fundamental
100. Island Venezuela
101. Jean — French actor
103. Make void
105. Cubic meter
106. The whole jury
107. Genus grasse
108. Australian cit
110. Pintail duck
112. Antitoxins
114. A tax
115. Baseba team
117. Jolson et al.
118. Stitch
120. — Cruces

134

PUZZLE 119

ACROSS

1 Mexican dishes
6 Noted for his wooden figureheads
10 He created Chicago's "Fountain of Time"
14 His work is in the Louvre
19 — committee
20 English painter
21 Swan genus
22 Papal veil
23 Quarter of a year (Scot.)
24 Founder of modern sculpture
26 He sculpted "Trois Graces"
27 Chemical suffix
28 Ireland
30 Code symbol
31 Unload trash
33 Golf position
34 Prize-winner for "Russian Dancers"
36 Poet and critic
38 Neptune's spear
40 Space vehicle
41 Vain
43 Curve of ship's planking
44 A bet
47 Beauty salon item
48 Likely
50 Coupled
54 Regarding
55 Golf great
56 Move stealthily
58 — Descartes
59 Born
60 Irish clans
61 Charles and Andrew
63 Sault — Marie
64 Certain beverage
66 Combine
67 He created the tomb of Philip the Bold
69 Requires
70 Cowardly animal
71 Guide
72 Tristram and —
74 Large artery
75 Louisiana politician
78 Annamese measure
79 A protamine (Biochem.)
81 June bugs (var.)
82 Contend
83 Greedy ones
85 Characterized by: a suffix
86 Peaceniks
87 Twining stem
88 Ethereal fluid
90 Except
91 Provide food
92 Facades
93 Electrified particle
95 Convalesce
97 Wire measure
98 Italian goldsmith and sculptor
102 Duke or Day
103 German artist, sculptor, playwright
107 French friend
108 Dispatched
110 But (L.)
111 Noted French sculptor
112 West or Murray
113 Headed bolt
115 Springtime purchase
118 Some revolve
120 French student
121 River in England
122 — Cassini
123 Fragrant rootstock
124 River to the North Sea
125 Trial
126 Blue or White
127 Diving bird

DOWN

1 Biblical name
2 "A Bell for — "
3 Tribal leader
4 Out, in Scotland
5 Plotter
6 Famous for "The Thinker"
7 Part of story opener
8 Biblical wilderness
9 Guillotine's victims
10 New Zealand thatching grass
11 One for —
12 Pen for sheep
13 Game fish
14 Crease in cricket
15 Swiss canton
16 Gall (Fr.)
17 Convey to a distance (var.)
18 Dogma
25 Sheer fabric
29 Symbol of Aries
32 Not "Miss"
35 Run away
36 Serfs
37 Catherine the Great
39 Beauty salon specialist
41 Mountains in Utah
42 Exhaust
44 To fly
45 Biblical name
46 He sculpted George Washington
47 Cheap cigars?
49 Detective (slang)
51 Yugoslav sculptor
52 Grafted (Her.)
53 Sly glance
55 Stream of spouting water
56 Indentation
57 Annoys pettily
60 Snathes (Scot.)
61 Kind of whip
62 Weaver's reeds
65 Lamprey
66 Irish character actor
68 Biblical name
70 Lifted with tackle
71 More certain
72 Body of Kaffir warriors
73 Levantine ketch
74 Love affair
75 Hang fluttering in air
76 Baseball team
77 Gives command to a horse
80 Law degree
81 Lavishes too much affection
84 Besmirch
86 American portrait sculptor
87 He did a life-size bust of Daniel Webster
89 Bluster or swagger
91 Centers
92 Andiron
94 Compass reading
96 Pet lamb
97 Insane
98 English poet
99 Mr. Zola
100 Dwells
101 Cast metal bar
103 Former tennis star
104 Love, in Rome
105 Indian of Venezuela
106 West German state
109 Real
111 Lively dance
114 December 24, for one
116 Ninny
117 Yale man
119 Hockey star

PUZZLE 120

ACROSS

1 For "The Old Maid" — 1935
6 For "Edith Wharton: A Biography" — 1976
11 For "The Founding of New England" — 1922
16 Dramatic
17 Conserve of grapes
18 For "Unfinished Business" — 1945
20 Alchemist's furnace
21 Sherry
22 Star in Scorpio
24 For "To Kill a Mockingbird" — 1961
26 Danewort
27 Declares
29 Eggs
30 — majesty
32 Arabian ruler
33 Arrow poison
34 Actor O'Neal
35 Hawaiian shrub
37 A ballet movement
38 Certain bills
40 Article of food
41 Strategic bridge holding
43 Fictional Simon
45 Mythical monsters
46 Start for pod or phone
48 Pollutes
49 Legendary Swiss patriot
50 Motherless calf
54 Black or green
55 Branch of biology
59 Heritable land
60 Stead (dial.)
62 Rail birds
64 Hawaiian island
65 Black gold
66 Biblical name
67 Larva of a certain fly
68 Faucet
69 A debauchee
71 For "Honey in the Horn" — 1936
72 New Zealand mollusks
75 Scottish Gaelic
76 Having no septa
78 Craggy hill
80 Boss, usually
82 River in England
83 Abdominal pain
85 "The Red"
86 Send back
89 Russian anarchist
91 Succumbs
95 Girl's name
96 Feature of a horse
97 God of love
99 Lifeless
100 For "Street Scene" — 1929
101 Drying oven
102 Doctrines
104 Cry of the bacchanals
105 WWII area
106 Whalebone
108 Cries, as a sheep
110 Suffix forming adjectives
111 Greek folk dance
113 Word with law or suit
115 Accepts a pension
117 High Jewish title
118 Spanish-American plain
119 Crafts
120 Agitates
121 It borders the Red Sea
122 Jewish month (var.)

DOWN

1 For "Present at the Creation" — 1970
2 Large parrot
3 Innate (Fr.)
4 She wept for her children
5 Shrivel (dial. Eng.)
6 Expensive rarities
7 December 31, et al.
8 " — and Peace"
9 Natives of: a suffix
10 Six-line stanzas
11 Lessens
12 One receiving a gift
13 Slaves and carpenters
14 Advanced degree
15 For "The Time of Your Life" — 1940
16 American novelist
19 A morocco leather
20 Apportion
23 Beaches
26 Rhythmical swing
28 Biblical name
31 Kind of paint
34 Bridge in Venice
36 Genus of maples
38 Ham it up
39 Spicy stews
40 Repulsive
42 Shield
44 Jumbled type
45 Early Roman clan
47 Put into action
49 Afternoon period
50 For "Collected Poems" — 1952
51 Farewell, in Madrid
52 Worth
53 Brewer's mash tub
55 Reach out blindly
56 Healing: comb. form
57 For "Harvey" — 1945
58 Start for human or highway
61 Roman 551
63 Kimono sash
70 Shoulder, in France
71 Mend
72 Fur piece
73 First hour of the day
74 Nimble
75 Geological era
77 To weary
79 Ancient
81 Roman 53
83 For "The Green Pastures" — 1930
84 Set of fixed bells
86 More unusual
87 Bok, for one
88 Trumpet creepers
89 For "Miss Lulu Bett" — 1921
90 Scent
92 Young hare
93 Male honeybees
94 Marks to let stand
96 Certain straw hats
98 Stings
101 A muntjac (India)
103 Cubic meter
106 Mistress of the house (India)
107 Blue or White
108 Part of N.B.
109 Hasty attempt
112 Tracking system
114 Cheat (slang)
116 Lupino or Cantor

PUZZLE 12.1

ACROSS

1 Stiffly decorous
5 Fundamental
10 Blaze
15 Dosages of absorbed radiation
19 Biblical word of reproach
20 Body of Moslem scholars
21 Actress: Ada —
22 Dill plant
23 Solar disk
24 With 27 Across, a luscious pie
25 Nautical word for "cease"
26 Occasion
27 See 24 Across
29 Star in Cygnus
31 Find it in fruit cake
33 Produced by inches
34 Coated with icing
35 Spanish peso
36 Yonder
39 Wild hogs
40 A stronghold
44 With 49 Down, tasty desserts
45 With 46 Across, apple pudding
46 See 45 Across
47 One — time
48 Titled nobleman
49 Start for act or port

50 Tiny arachnids
51 Where 58 Across is cooked
52 Netherlands commune
53 Badgers
54 Devil's food, et al.
55 Large
56 Dieter's downfall
58 With 59 Across, a delicious dessert
59 See 58 Across
60 Walkway
61 Sits for an artist
62 Russian city
63 Beer mugs
66 Classifies
67 Used in taffy
71 Honor prices (Ancient Irish Law)
72 Eagle's home
73 Capital of Oregon
74 Palm leaf (var.)
75 Boorish
76 Daughter of Ops and Saturn
77 Rail birds
78 Night, in Paris
79 Anger
80 Dieter's nemesis
81 Voracious fish
82 Sweet, sticky cake

83 Rhetorical
85 Small, sweet cake
86 Studs
87 Praline feature
88 Seagoing vessels
89 Painful
90 Spanish seaport
93 Ranch animals
94 More absorbent
98 An astringent
99 Fasten again
101 Name in baseball
103 Diva's forte
104 Cotton cloth
105 Valleys
106 Moroccan seaport
107 Famous WWI sergeant
108 Look askance
109 To lay away
110 Corset supports
111 Snick and —

DOWN

1 Baby carriage
2 Assess
3 One who often licks the spoon
4 Multifarious
5 Swelled out
6 Member of the Unalaska tribe
7 Sewn (Her.)
8 I love (L.)
9 Property statutes

10 French gold coins
11 Morning reception
12 King of Israel
13 Feast day: comb. form
14 Commits
15 Allotment
16 Cuckoos
17 Half: a prefix
18 British gun
26 Hawaiian goose
30 Merit
32 Imitative of art
34 Hired things
35 Sweet fruits found in bread
36 Bundled
37 The aftersong
38 Belgian city
39 Unruly children
40 Entertained
41 Roof edges
42 Menu item
43 — Clara
45 B'nai —
46 Often ridden
49 See 44 Across
50 Creates
51 Certain examinations
53 Navy and kidney
54 Social division
55 Shine brightly
57 Kind of cake
58 Actor Karloff
59 City in France

61 One studying intently
62 Kind of tea
63 Fine line of a letter
64 Seaport of Nova Scotia
65 Sea duck
66 Pinnacle of glacier ice
67 To wed
68 Whiskey drinks
69 The choice part
70 Gluts
72 Shield
73 Steeps
76 Sweet egg concoctions
77 Those seeking bargains
78 Small bouquets
80 Cozy
81 Silk, in Paris
82 Ripped
84 To charm
85 Ingredient of a rich cake
86 Raises
88 More timid
89 Floral piece
90 Shaded walk
91 Nautical word
92 Crescent-shaped figure
93 French city
94 Biblical country
95 Metallic element
96 Ireland
97 Roue
100 Consume
102 Large cistern

PUZZLE 122

ACROSS

1 Oriental nurse
5 Thick slice
9 Droops
13 Scottish Highlander
17 Netherlands commune
18 Italian town
19 Noted film critic
20 Beginning
22 Horse opera
23 Kind of piano
25 Aquatic animal
26 Tourist's delight
28 Imposing
30 Girl of song
31 Hawaiian city
32 Cain's land
34 State in France
35 Favorite
36 Roman patriot'
37 Attica townships
39 Heroic in scale
41 "The —"; romance by Scott
44 Clique
46 Slowly, in music
50 Zodiac sign
51 Camper's bed
52 Refuse of grapes
54 Mistake
55 Diving bird
56 Covered avenue
59 Muck
61 Evans or Robertson
62 Chang and —
63 Most lucid
65 Merges
67 Iranian coins
69 Hamlet, et al.
71 Evening, in Germany
72 Most elegant
75 Temporary intermissions
77 Theater sign
80 Pealed
81 Slang affirmative
83 Impassive
84 Shine
85 Mountain chain
87 Caroline island group
89 Explorer Johnson
90 List of candidates
91 Religious festival
93 Base
96 Discernment
97 Spruce
99 Dwellings
100 Concerning, in a letter
101 Dine
104 Wild ox
106 Afternoon party
107 Arrow poison
108 Even score
111 Extended educational trip
114 City in Michigan
117 Frozen
118 Bartender's need
120 Apportions
121 Short fishing line
122 Priest of Lhasa
123 Paradise
124 Expunge
125 To corner
126 Biblical name
127 Pub missile
128 Dwarf

DOWN

1 Palm cockatoo
2 Gold or silver
3 Arabian gulf
4 Construction workers
5 The tarpon
6 Spanish plain
7 Girl's nickname
8 Rifle adjunct
9 Patriotic org.
10 Biblical king
11 Category
12 Staid
13 Christmas (obs.)
14 Against
15 Prevent
16 Release (obs.)
17 Swamps
21 Weight allowance
24 Aphorism
27 Quote
29 California city
33 Skin: a suffix
36 City in France
37 Foolish old person
38 Thailand
40 Designer Pierre
41 To blanch
42 Kind of will?
43 U.S. border river
44 Source of cocaine
45 "The Red"
47 Bridge triumph
48 Captive of Hercules
49 Crude metals
51 Torch holder
53 Part of Yugoslavia
56 Bowling lane
57 Beloved
58 Serfs, of old
60 Set in matter
63 Bounder
64 Examine
66 Egyptian god
68 Take food
70 Found in sewing boxes
72 — Spee
73 Hindu queen
74 Medieval Italian coin
76 Girl's name
78 Noise of surf on shore
79 Actor: Reginald —
82 Actor O'Brian
84 An adhesive
86 Sit astride
88 Granny, for one
90 Headline
92 Vulgar contraction·
94 Greek letter
95 Bewhiskered
96 Biblical name
98 Barney —
100 Set in from the margin
101 Ova
102 Common contraction
103 Old German coin
105 Of the ear
107 Interior
108 The sun personified
109 That is (L.)
110 Being
112 Blue or White
113 San —, Italy
115 Verdi opera
116 Andean country
119 Girl's nickname

142

PUZZLE 123

ACROSS

1 Successor of Ruth
6 Picnic pests
11 Body of Moslem scholars
16 Singer Tebaldi
17 Hindu queen
18 Hockey star
20 Batter's hope
21 Sacred images
22 Sprinkle around
24 An islet
25 Biblical name
27 Social events
29 Home of 14 Down
30 Gen. Arnold, to friends
31 English river
32 Tilden, of tennis
33 Make choice
34 Spartan king
36 Hinge joint
37 Crazes
39 Snick and —
40 Ascot, that is
42 Lively dances
43 Golf star: Gary —
45 Inland sea
46 Testators name them
47 Indigent
48 Fine violins
51 A dead body (Poetic)
52 Ferry charge
56 English author
57 Cant of thieves
58 Sticky cake
59 Low haunt
60 Drug addict
61 Wide
62 Open lesions
63 Mountain, in France
64 See 46 Down
65 Pro football Hall of Fame star
66 Olympic swimming star
67 Star in Hockey Hall of Fame
68 Starlike body
70 To spend or pass
71 Waxy ointment
72 Actress: Cheryl —
73 Fumes
74 — breve (music)
75 Its capital is Papeete
78 Aristocratic
79 Persons of little importance
83 Region
84 Kind of paint
86 Appear
87 TV show
88 Spring month, in Paris
89 Jewish month
90 Wild pig
91 Middle East country (abbr.)
92 Formerly (archaic)
94 Treasury agt.
95 Frigid
97 Tennis star
98 Ancient kingdom
100 Invigorating
102 Prairie wolves
104 Skill
105 Sultan's decree
106 Expiates
107 Under, to a poet
108 Colonist's news source
109 Nominated

DOWN

1 In the manner of certain fables
2 Pickler's plant
3 Stadium cheer
4 American inventor
5 Baseball league
6 Pro football Hall of Fame star
7 Mother-of-pearl
8 Wild ox
9 Football's "Big — "
10 Certain lyrical poems
11 College in New Jersey
12 Folds over
13 An age
14 Baseball team
15 Bowling star
16 Dosage of X-rays
19 Indian tent (var.)
20 Irish playwright
23 Appraiser
26 Petitioner
28 Ancient Greek country
32 Vermont city
35 Dorothy Hamill, for one
36 Large parrots
37 Damp
38 Lacrosse and curling
39 Hindu garment
41 Legal instrument
42 King of Judea
44 Learning
46 With 64 Across, a golf great
47 Former president of Chile
48 Island off Venezuela
49 Hebrew prophet
50 Deputy
51 Lots of people
52 Strong point
53 Ethiopian town
54 Civetlike animal
55 Between (Fr.)
57 Plant of the arum family
58 Labors
61 Jim Thorpe Trophy winner
62 Ear of grain
63 Ethics
65 Obnoxious child
66 Outer covering
67 American inventor
69 Charles Lamb
70 Bowling great
71 Taciturn person
73 Fanciful
74 Baseball league
75 Domesticates
76 Ark's dock?
77 Famous football coach
78 Nothing, in Spain
79 Install in office
80 Palmed off
81 Allergy symptoms
82 Belgian town
85 Football great
86 Popular sport
90 Aisle star
93 Story
94 Pale tinge
95 Philippine termite (var.)
96 A kind of Philippine fort
97 First-rate
99 The turmeric
101 Hockey star
103 — Kippur

144

PUZZLE 124

ACROSS

1 Costumes
6 Singer Vikki
10 Storm
14 To dismay
19 Ascended
20 Wings
21 Idi —
22 Betel palm
23 Joiners
25 Skilled artisans
27 Patron saint
   of 25 Across
28 Unwind, in
   a way
30 Look for
31 Satisfy
32 Low haunt
33 Neglect
34 Elevator cage
36 Levantine
   ketch
38 Abbrs. on maps
39 Degree
40 Indians
42 Van's opposite
44 Ornamental
   spangle
47 Patron saint
   of 69 Across
49 Man's name
53 Patron saint
   of barbers
54 Sea slug genus
55 German river
57 Kitchen need
58 Med. school
   subj.
59 A fruit
60 Man's name
62 The sweetsop

63 Postscripts
   (abbr.)
64 Makes
   resistance
66 Omar, et al.
67 Art cult
68 African river
69 Cobblers
75 Recline
   awkwardly
78 Viper
81 Source of
   karakul
82 Dormouse
83 Wainscots
84 Stead
85 Regions
87 Persian
   demigod
88 Part of B.A.
89 Takes the
   part of
90 Patron saint
   of 116 Across
92 Patron saint
   of musicians
94 Patron saint
   of 23 Across
95 Sense organs
97 Scotch fisher-
   men's huts
   (obs. var.)
98 Patron saint
   of 65 Across
99 Inferior (Fr.)
102 Wide smile
104 Senhor (abbr.)
105 A fool (slang)
106 Wager
109 Word in
   Mark 15:34

111 Pearl Buck
   heroine
113 Indolent
115 Network
116 Homemakers
119 They mend
   locks
121 Its capital
   is Shillong
122 Grotto
123 Fencing sword
124 Group of eight
125 Approaches
126 King or Alda
127 Germ
128 Wallace or Noah

DOWN

1 Sped
2 Papal veil
3 Nonmetallic
   element
4 Catch sight of
5 Bishopric
6 Feline treat
7 Wide awake
8 Steak order
9 Surgical
   operations
10 Roofing slate
11 Hebrew prophet
12 Patron saint
   of beggars
13 Make beloved
14 Dutch measure
15 Stiffly proper
16 Patron saint
   of 119 Across
17 Suffered pain
18 Used by
   69 Across
24 Divine spirit

26 Heavens
29 Asiatic country
33 American
   inventor
35 Iterate
37 Panthers
39 Outfit with
   clothes
40 Photographic
   developer
41 Walk crabwise
46 Film worker's
   headache
44 A rebuff
45 Eternities
46 Russian beer
   (var.)
47 Nat King —
46 A gas
50 Citizen's
   privilege
51 Always
52 Headland
54 Famous heart
   surgeon
56 Religious
   ceremonials
60 Award for
   heroism
61 Mergansers
64 Aries
66 Entire amount
67 Formal
   argument
68 Bridge triumph
70 — kiri
71 Hebrew
   measure
72 "The Red"
73 Bellows (obs.)
74 Neat piles

75 Loggers use
   them
76 Mohammedan
   fairies
77 Patron saint of
   the impossible
78 Assistant
79 Ooze
80 Thrust forward
84 Austrian
   girl's name
86 Rug surface
89 Dinner course
91 Direction
   indicator
93 Electrified
   particles
94 Patron saint
   of netmakers
96 Dioxide of
   silicon
98 Stabbed
99 Irish play-
   wright
100 European shad
101 Composer-
   bandmaster
103 Nautical
105 Silver in
   ingots (var.)
106 Actress Davis
107 Anesthetic
108 Irritable
110 Bavarian river
112 Russian river
114 John Paul II
115 Cereal grain
117 Printer's
   measures
118 Oriental coin
120 Unruly crowd

PUZZLE 125

ACROSS

1 Used to create
9 Down
5 Arrangement
10 Atelier item
15 Farm implement
19 Comedienne Adams
20 One of the Muses
21 She wept for her children
22 Rural path
23 A grave
24 Solvent for certain artists
25 Social group
26 Nick Charles' pet
27 Singer: Licia —
29 Three: a prefix
31 City in Maine
33 Flatfish
34 An instant
36 Pub missile
37 Chalk for Degas
40 Makes soundproof
42 Herb of the aster family
46 Photographic developer
47 Send in payment
48 Young boy
50 Clamor
51 Weights of India
52 To induce
53 Biblical name
55 Mention
56 Old French coin
57 Misrepresent
58 Public servant
60 Faucet
61 To taste
63 Warble
65 Large-billed birds
67 Grain crop
69 Reserved
71 Killed
72 Embroidery material
76 Bone: comb. form
78 A copy
82 Haggard novel
83 Newts or efts
85 Worship
87 Knave of clubs
88 Early dweller in Britain
90 Lady's garment, in ancient Rome
91 Prevarication
92 Drudge
93 Habituate
95 Chemical suffix
96 Gush out
97 Silly people
98 Sea nymph
100 Charlotte, Emily and Anne
102 A thurible
103 Region
105 — prosequi

106 Dispatched
107 Gifts
111 Mountain pass
112 Desert driver
116 Japanese aborigine
117 Of the ilium
119 Ham it up
121 Within: comb. form
122 Musical prince
123 Mud volcano
124 Style of type
125 Hasty attempt
126 Demolish
127 Animal fat
128 Tax
129 Large volume

DOWN

1 Greek mountain chain
2 Baal, for one
3 Tree branch
4 August (Gr.)
5 English author
6 Expunge
7 With 54 Down, a London sight
8 Indian
9 Painted from a model
10 Lure
11 Melody
12 To corrupt
13 Receded
14 Room for action
15 Metal breastplate
16 Cobbler's need
17 Upon
18 Alienate
28 Christmas carol
30 Fissure
32 Persia
34 Artist's medium
35 Enroll
37 Sits for
9 Down
38 Betel palm
39 Play a guitar
40 Resign (Scot.)
41 Dried orchid tubers
43 Lariat
44 Founder of the Ottoman empire
46 Cries
47 Electrical unit
49 Attica townships
52 Seesaws
53 To guide
54 See 7 Down
57 Explosion
58 "The Mill on the —"
59 Relative
62 Kentucky bluegrass
64 Actress Massey
66 Hundredweight (abbr.)
68 Blow the nose (Scot.)
70 Facial aspect
72 Colorado resort

73 River in Germany
74 Return
75 Jacket and collar
77 Scents
79 Belgian town
80 Hesitate
81 Found in a dying fire
84 Liquid part of fat
86 Table scrap
89 Fictional island
91 School books
92 Mildest
94 Ireland
96 French town
97 Tierney or Tunney
99 Actress Darcel
101 Active sport
102 Bond of union
104 Burden-bearer
106 Old Nick
107 Couple
108 Capital of Latvia
109 Grandson of Adam
110 Dregs
112 Arrive
113 Within: comb. form
114 Dutch cheese
115 Dress of state
118 Peer Gynt's mother
120 Witty saying

148

PUZZLE 126

ACROSS

1 Monk's hood
5 Blemish
10 The Pentateuch
15 Charge against a G.I.
19 French girlfriend
20 American short story writer
21 Architectural molding
22 Agave fiber
23 Sailing vessel
25 Anemones
27 Degree in theology
28 Pindar wrote them
29 Female sheep
31 Partly inundated forest
32 John — Passos
33 Barlow novel
35 Rows
37 Stonecrop
39 Higher than diamonds and clubs
41 Ransoms
43 Leave
46 Sits for one's portrait
47 Plays on words
48 Code symbols
50 More rational
51 Being
52 Dispatch
53 Equine meal
55 French town
56 Peer Gynt's mother

57 Sow bug
59 Layers
61 Partner of long.
62 Condensed statements
64 Cattle farm
66 Cereal grasses
68 Treat hides
69 June bug
70 Merry
71 Poltroons
75 Ishmael's mother
77 Covered with moisture
81 Slender finial
82 Scope
84 Plural of genus
86 Labor org.
87 Force
89 Render turbid
90 Seines
91 Weather word
92 Mountain chain
94 Biblical name
96 Dagger
97 Sponge (colloq.)
98 Feel displeasure
100 Marked to let stand
102 Elevates
103 Lifeless
105 Sudden gush
106 Street game
107 Droop
109 Unfledged bird
111 Undivided

112 Miss Hepburn, to friends
113 Bombycid moths
116 Hayrakes
119 Lady of the fan
122 Philippine termite
123 Combine
124 Arabian chieftain (var.)
125 — above
126 Quarterless slipper
127 English auto "shoes"
128 Tries to lose weight
129 Paradise

DOWN

1 Cries, like a crow
2 Neglect
3 Hoisting machines
4 Conducted
5 Phantoms
6 More docile
7 Fortifies
8 Native of: a suffix
9 Sea nymphs
10 Rose to a great height
11 Egg: comb. form
12 Indo-Chinese language
13 Robert and Alan

14 Jumped
15 The wallaba
16 Windbreak (Forestry)
17 Palindromic name
18 Young girl
24 Spike or Tom
26 Mineral deposits
30 Tiny
34 — fixe
35 Softhearted
36 Unruffled
38 Javanese tree
39 Asparagus stalk
40 Sheriff's band
41 A dwarf
42 Asterisk
44 Kind of race
45 Jogs
47 Vegetables
49 Dagger thrust
52 Slim
54 Persons of long experience
57 Chic
58 Detecting device
59 Scrawny one
60 Plowed land
63 Actress: — Hagen
65 Wooden peg
67 Lixivium
71 Coniferous tree
72 Suppose

73 Weather Bureau system
74 Road sign
75 Spartan serfs
76 Milk curdler
77 — noire
78 Protective pane
79 Eulogy
80 American financier
83 Hastens
85 Require
88 Numerical suffix
91 Levantine ketch
93 Scoff
95 Rests
96 Scattered
97 Provide food
99 Kind of audition
101 Large cask
102 Appraisers
104 Dusky
106 Youngest son
107 Became dizzy
108 Japanese aborigine
110 Biblical name
112 Leg joint
114 Voided escutcheon
115 — O'Casey
117 Stain
118 Abbr. on map
120 Wurttemberg measure
121 West or Murray

ACROSS
1 Hand toy
5 Miss Bernhardt
10 Throwing game
15 Resorts
19 Avouch
20 Insect stage
21 English novelist
22 Scream
23 Metallic element
24 Spring flower
25 Child's game
26 Appraise
27 Made a mistake
29 Soap-frame bar
30 Is in debt
31 Engaged
32 Running matches
34 Lettuce
36 Cuttlefish
38 Chinese pagoda
41 Short-napped
42 Two-wheeled vehicle
44 Patriotic org.
45 Hebrew letter
48 Instantly important
50 Genus of grasses
52 Occultism
54 Wild creatures
55 Street game
56 Force
58 French painter
59 Against
60 God of the Mohammedans
61 Spaghetti
63 Hoarfrost
64 Street game
66 Female swan
67 Child's card game
69 Ascend
70 Child's game
71 Narrated
72 Child's game
76 Kick the —
77 Jumper's delight
82 — and seek
83 Hindu guitar
85 A cap (var.)
86 Turkish regiment
87 Winged
89 Spool for thread
90 Tenement districts
91 Use block letters
92 Repulses
94 A basis of argument
96 Woolly
97 Winter time in N.Y.
98 Fuel
100 Goddess of peace
101 Dance or Valley
102 John — Passos
103 Child's game
105 With 106 Across, a street game
106 See 105 Across
108 Clayey
111 Unsorted wheaten flour
113 Post
115 A pry
119 Secondhand
120 Famous Gertrude
121 Soothe
123 Commanded
124 Temple
125 Listened to
126 Relative
127 Ireland
128 Astaire or MacMurray
129 Girl's name (poss.)
130 Sometimes chosen, in games
131 Tardy

DOWN
1 Ivy League college
2 At an end
3 Period of time
4 Law's companion
5 Command to a dog
6 Entertains
7 Chest sounds
8 Spartan king
9 Street game
10 Deponent
11 Below (Naut.)
12 Ceremonies
13 Prepares a salad
14 Farm enclosure
15 Ancient country in Asia
16 Pome fruit
17 "Der — " (Adenauer)
18 Child's delight, in winter
28 Mends
31 King of Tyre
33 One old —
35 Brilliant-colored fish
37 Leather moccasin
38 Band instruments
39 Common contraction
40 Pea tree
42 Gold or silver
43 Living room piece
45 Madness
46 Fragrant oleoresin
47 Matched
49 "The Red"
50 Room, in Paris
51 Sloths
53 Yeast formed on brewing liquors
55 Of the ancient Greeks and Romans
57 Movie zanies
60 "— Irish Rose"
61 Mumblety - —
62 Apportion
65 A language of Liberia
66 God of flocks
68 Dentist's degree
70 Sailor
71 Singer: Mel —
72 Stock unit
73 Used in mah-jongg
74 Conform
75 Head (Fr.)
76 Romantic isle
77 Hesitation
78 Mountain lake
79 Homer opus
80 Division of a long poem
81 Flown by children
84 Child's toy
85 With 108 Down, a child's game
88 English composer
90 Pintail duck
91 The whole jury
93 Indian
95 Necessary trips
96 Broadway play
99 Needed on rinks
101 To console
103 Worn out
104 Supplier of energy
106 Angered
107 One resisting authority
108 See 85 Down
109 Eskers
110 Smooth
112 Become weary
114 Et — ; and others
116 Spanish measure
117 Redact
118 Descartes
120 Haggard novel
122 An affirmative

PUZZLE 128

ACROSS
1 G.I. meal
5 Greek island
10 Facts from yore
11 Abrade
12 Islands off Galway
13 Babbled
14 Vulcan's creation
16 Silkworm of Assam
17 Back talk
18 Elec. unit
19 Usurp
22 Cut of pasta
23 Elec. terminal
24 Lasso
25 Duration
26 Roman ruler
27 "— was going to St. Ives"
28 Foundation
29 Man's nickname
30 Mediocre
35 Slothful
37 Romanian city
38 Filched
39 Wee bit
40 Landmark (Sp.)
41 Yemen's capital

DOWN
1 Bang
2 Israeli dance
3 Algerian city
4 Betake oneself
5 Discard
6 Macaw
7 Fabric
8 Herbert's specialty
9 Chancel seats
11 Sail holder
15 Greek flask
19 Liqueur
20 Sphere of control
21 Poem
22 Oriental cymbal
23 Stymied
24 Inelegant
26 Number
28 Swiss city
31 Vishnu incarnation
32 Dry
33 Portal
34 Actress Barbara
36 Palm leaf

154

PUZZLE 129

ACROSS
1 Attired
5 Greek letter
10 Turbulence
11 Put on cassette
13 Prayer ending
14 Off the ship
15 Storage box
16 Outcry in Bonn
17 Hammarskjold
18 Ring-shaped island
20 Arab official
21 Inlet (Scot.)
22 Imprison
23 Candle
26 "I Remember Mama" star
27 Jewish month
28 Drunkard
29 Mein —!
30 Correct a text
33 Now (It.)
34 Outstanding
35 Lummox
37 Like Junior's bed
39 Latitude
40 Became lachrymose
41 Before (Lat.)
42 Humming sound
43 Rind

DOWN
1 Sourpuss
2 Greek city
3 Means
4 Lair
5 Advisor at Delphi
6 Netting
7 Plane formation (abbr.)
8 "King of Swing"
9 Indict
12 M.D., B.A. or LL.B.
16 Indonesian island
19 Manifest
20 Shrewd
23 Embarrass a base-stealer
24 Bedecked
25 East Indian vessel
26 Cupola
28 Leave the Union
31 Not a soul
32 Literary giant
34 Yemen seaport
36 Have a hunch
38 Nigerian
39 Kill (sl.)

155

PUZZLE 130

ACROSS
1 Exclusive group
6 Hell
11 Counter-tenors
12 Originated
13 Initiate
14 Fry somewhat
15 Film Hunter
16 Leap, as a frog
18 Bakery product
19 Gone above
21 Strip of pine
22 Man's nickname
23 Demigod
24 Salt tree
25 "Maude" co-star
26 Tennis great
27 Elephant's cry
28 Check
29 Zeal
31 Cry audibly
32 Greek letter
33 Salt (Fr.)
35 Love poetry muse
37 Japanese-American
39 More lovable
40 Pupil (Fr.)
41 Hoodwinked
42 Temptress

DOWN
1 Dramatis personae
2 Wedding setting
3 Betray
4 Craggy hill
5 Lover of beauty
6 Fastening device
7 Altar constel-lation
8 Traitor
9 Sea inlet
10 Taken care of
17 Unified
20 Oregon city
21 Pottery fragment
24 Oregon city
25 Service men
26 Acquiesce
27 Nonsense!
30 Distaff ruff
32 Trite humor
34 Debtor's burden
36 To a —
38 Asian river

PUZZLE 131

ACROSS

1 — the cud
5 Box
9 Stockings
10 Exonerate
12 Scatter-
   brained
15 King (Sp.)
16 Egyptian
   god
17 Fish
18 Ornamental
   pattern
19 "Where
   the
   Boys—"
20 Hackney
   coach
23 Particle
24 Entering
25 Portion
26 Eight
   (Ger.)
27 Terrified
29 Andress
   film
30 Indian
   title
31 City on
   the
   Ohio.
   (abbr.)
32 Rascal
33 Gershwin
36 Flavoring
   substance
39 Judicial
   symbol
40 Olive
   tree
   genus
41 Not one
42 Tuesday in
   Hollywood

DOWN

1 "Silkwood"
   co-star
2 Residence
3 Sight
4 Moisten
5 Artifice
6 New cadet
7 Tree fiber
8 Heat
   source
11 British
   royal
   symbol
13 French
   river
14 Considered
18 Highlander
20 Complete
   failure
21 Advancing
   by
   degrees
22 Greek
23 Muslim
   prayer
   call
27 In plain
   words
28 Guitar
   device
30 Earth
   worker
33 Otiose
34 Whirl
35 Romanian
   city
37 Eggs
38 Holy
   smoke!

157

PUZZLE 132

ACROSS

1 Merchant guild (var.)
6 Leave undone
10 Violently
11 Campfire residue
13 Keep reserved
15 "Now We —Six"
16 Fate
17 Moisten
18 With (Ger.)
19 Inclination
20 Tea cake
22 Uttered
23 Milburn of "Gunsmoke"
24 Greek island
25 Breathe heavily
26 Kind of bear
27 Gaelic
28 English river
29 Outside (prefix)
30 Go—binge
31 Bar habitue
34 He fumes and frets?
37 Therefore
38 Type face
39 Agitate
40 Gen. Curtis —

DOWN

1 Sound of mirth
2 Swedish wine measure
3 Church part
4 You (Ger.)
5 Type of dye
6 Schooner feature
7 Adherent (suffix)
8 Poured out
9 Musical composition
12 Colonize
14 Communication
18 Card game
19 Carried
20 Carbohydrates
21 Incessant
23 Lecture
24 Chewy candy
26 Plays with words
30 Sunday punch
31 Read hastily
32 Greek mountains
33 Three, in cards
35 Here (Fr.)
36 "—Buttermilk Sky"

158

PUZZLE 133

ACROSS

1 African lake
5 Nursery fixture
9 Fatherland
10 Valentine symbol
12 Indonesian island
13 Poor
15 Dupin's "George Sand"
17 Written letter
18 Notion
19 Woman's name
20 College course
24 Canaanite deity
25 Frolic
26 Suit fabric
27 Coup d' —
28 Cain was one
29 Trouble
30 Shinto temple
31 Vineyard (Fr.)
32 Excitement
37 Radiator
39 Counter-tenor
40 Anesthetic
41 Jewish nation
42 Slippery
43 Adhesive

DOWN

1 Fellow
2 Ace in the —
3 Egyptian deity
4 Actor, Bruce —
5 Tolled
6 — Adoree
7 Author Fleming
8 Priest's book
11 In one's early years
14 Distributor
16 Biblical brother
20 Moralize
21 Pensioner
22 Appraise
23 Convened
24 Arthur of "Maude"
26 Bridge coup
28 Wine type
30 Metal
33 Beyond
34 "Essays of —"
35 Surcease
36 Resiliency
38 Word often in a title

159

PUZZLE 134

ACROSS

1 Piece of work
6 Weapon
9 Inamorata
10 Bard
12 Circumvent
13 Braid
15 Clammy
16 Trifling
17 Annul, as a law
20 Buddy
21 Possess
22 Faction
23 Sci-fi creature
26 Merriment
27 American jurist
28 Scary shout
29 Night previous
30 Nimrod
33 "— Antigua" ('56 song)
35 Hat (sl.)
37 Mine roof
38 By oneself
40 American patriot
41 Store
42 Bob and —
43 Give birth to

DOWN

1 Skein of yarn
2 Be imminent
3 Egg-shaped
4 Fiery
5 Before
6 Dismay (Brit. spelling)
7 Kaiser, e.g.
8 Pasty
11 Philippic
14 Texas city
16 Criticize
18 Still water
19 Lambkin's ma
22 Photo
23 Lobster's claw
24 Sumptuous
25 Brigadier's symbol
26 Swindle
28 Sweet roll
30 Full of punctures
31 Slur over
32 Wrinkle
34 Bartok
36 Legal document
38 Priest's garb
39 Spanish composer

160

PUZZLE 135

ACROSS

1 Saintly symbol
5 Contemplate
11 Culture medium
12 Hardy
13 "— caput mundi"
14 Salty
15 Age
16 Slower (Mus.)
17 Nabokov novel
18 Nautical rope
20 Dickens character
21 Greek letter
22 Translation
23 German city
25 "Lulu" composer
26 Moon (Lat.)
27 Native of a place
28 Rowan tree
29 Reach
33 Call — day
34 Light beam
35 Maxim
36 One kind of jacket
38 Exasperate
39 Revenue
40 Unused
41 Required
42 Honey drink

DOWN

1 Pasha's place
2 Plato's marketplace
3 Texas statesman
4 Openings (Anat.)
5 "Barber of Seville" heroine
6 Make proud
7 Man's nickname
8 Lindbergh was one
9 Extracting
10 Bemused
16 Actress Gam
19 "Victory" heroine
22 Confined
23 De Sade heroine
24 Heighten
25 Too thin
26 Stored
27 Glided
29 White sauce
30 Out of the way
31 — lily
32 Harris, e.g.
37 Doze off
38 Border

161

PUZZLE 136

ACROSS
1 Police action
5 Memorable years
8 Different
9 Pamphlet
11 Observed
12 Redford
14 Pungent
15 Newspaper employee
16 A Bronte
18 Reverence
19 Eschewed food
22 —service
23 Daisylike flower
24 Food fish
26 Colorado Indian
27 Sissified
28 Intimidate
29 Enter
30 Blackboard item
32 Dutch cheese
36 Albanian capital
37 Enthuse
38 Said further
39 Egyptian deity
40 "Quiet on the—!"
41 Afford

DOWN
1 Remainder
2 Athena's title
3 Czech river
4 Toothed (Zool.)
5 Disintegrate
6 Nobel Prize physicist
7 Man-made fabrics
9 Tendency
10 Mason's implements
13 Covenant
17 Saul's relative
19 Spigot
20 Oregon city
21 Airline employees
24 Indian title
25 Iolite or spinel
27 —over (studied)
29 Dramatist, Jean —
31 Marquis de —
33 British title
34 English river
35 Set right

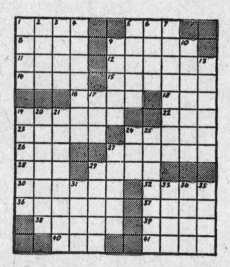

PUZZLE 137

ACROSS
1 Ness
5 Leafy fare
10 Asian river
11 Biological groups
12 Vatican office
13 Require
14 Threefold (pref.)
15 German river
16 Racket
18 Bird's beak
21 Resolve
23 Shopping area
24 Dodge
25 Famed soprano
26 Dregs
27 Feminist, Kate —
28 Sandy's cry
29 Extensive view
30 Spark producer
32 Evil
35 Comfy
37 Cheap cigar (sl.)
38 Clergyman's title
39 English river
40 Inviting word

41 Roman highway

DOWN
1 Dray
2 Love (Sp.)
3 Activate
4 Time period
5 Apprehend
6 Poker term
7 Study

8 Biblical lion
9 Indian fodder plant
11 Gaggle's members
15 Feral
17 American patriot

19 European river
20 Sheep's cry
21 Hall (Sp.)
22 At all
23 Liquefy
25 Haze
27 Earth worker

29 Helmet part
31 Delayed
33 Church part
34 Stag
35 "Just the Way You —"
36 Denary
37 King (Fr.)

163

PUZZLE 138

ACROSS

1 "Pistol-Packin'—"
5 Wild Ox
9 Winged
11 Strike (sl.)
13 Cheapskate
14 Strict
15 Majors or Marvin
16 Actress Charlotte
18 Morse Code sound
19 New member
21 Remote
22 Quest
23 Table d'—
24 Perfume
26 Soupy food
27 Float
28 Judge's bench
29 Luau baking pit
30 Actor Meredith
33 Apiece
34 Harem chamber
35 Woman's name
36 Tiny one
38 Poe's sleuth
40 Legislator
41 Save wedding costs
42 English river
43 City of Manasseh

DOWN

1 Kind of syrup
2 Foreign
3 Lock horns
4 Had lunch
5 Defeat
6 Traitor
7 Coerced
8 Marked with lines
10 Wandering
12 Diner's choice
17 Emmet
20 Wee one
23 Suspended
24 Strikes
25 Redgrave film
26 Easter event
28 Lad
30 House-maid (Fr.)
31 Game bird
32 Less irrational
37 Action (suff.)
39 The gums

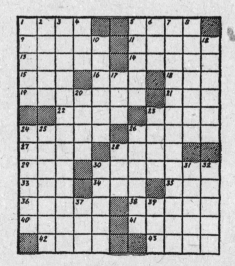

PUZZLE 139

ACROSS
1 Muslin official
5 Luminary
9 Geraldine — Ferraro
10 Winter need
12 Father —
13 Asian wild sheep
14 Wallach
15 Excavated
16 But (Lat.)
17 Chianti, e.g.
19 Henpeck
20 Turf
21 Abject
22 Deep pink
24 Desiccated
25 English river
26 Actor John
27 Man's nickname
28 Louver
31 Go wrong
32 One (Ger.)
33 Prior to (pref.)
34 Soccer team
36 Baby's utterance
37 Acclivity
38 Frosting device

39 Catch sight of
40 Italian river

DOWN
1 Provide party foods
2 Old-woman-ish

3 Halfway there
4 Scottish river
5 Twilled fabric
6 Kids' game
7 Slowly
8 Press statement

10 Frequent
11 Wrinkled
15 Telephone part
18 Withdraw
21 Kind of muffin
22 Profession
23 Stretch across

24 "Giant" star
26 Accompany
28 Itsy-bitsy
29 Command
30 Stiller's partner
35 Big shot
36 Clangor

PUZZLE 140

ACROSS
1 Abstinent
6 Indian abode
11 French river
12 Scot. island
13 Engraved
14 French seaport
15 Guided
16 Network
18 Knightly title
19 Cheerfully
21 Perceive
22 Zola novel
23 Amalgamate
24 Boundary
25 Drayman's vehicle
26 Stood up
27 Dullard
28 Written letter
29 Back out
31 Fondle
32 Sculpture or music
33 Not cooked
35 Smyrna figs
37 Plato's marketplace
39 Alps (Ger.)
40 "I — have danced all night..."
41 Irritable
42 Cassettes

DOWN
1 Doorway part
2 Willow
3 Hold a course
4 Before
5 Valpolicella, e.g.
6 Puss
7 Go wrong
8 Special interest people
9 Least challenging
10 Dinner course
17 High note
20 Glut
23 Make out
24 German wine
25 Reach
26 Iterate
27 Jujube
29 Pluvious
30 American painter
34 Bankrolls
36 Convened
38 Tibetan gazelle

PUZZLE 141

ACROSS
1 Rabbit
5 Bengal or bent
10 Along in years
11 Merited
13 Be destined
15 Chemistry suffix
16 Poem
17 Tenth of a sen
18 Expiated
20 Chinese lake
21 French shooting match
22 Party
23 Fundamental
26 Gists
27 "The Red"
28 Japanese measure
29 Soul (Fr.)
30 Pitcher's pitch
33 Man's nickname
34 Prompt
35 Italian TV-Radio network
37 Show of solidarity
40 Languishing
41 Advantage
42 Type size
43 Regard

DOWN
1 Sound of mirth
2 Guam's capital
3 Construct with sandbags
4 Dutch commune
5 Sex; class
6 Eradicated
7 Skill
8 Short drink
9 Arranged in series
12 Repudiates
14 Column style
19 Of the ear
22 Nourishment
23 Take courage
24 Ancient Asian country
25 Attacking
26 Leader
28 Mud
30 Perfume
31 Wear away
32 Pasture
36 Detail
38 Aunt (Sp.)
39 Communist

PUZZLE 142

ACROSS

1 Syrian city
5 Soprano Lucine
10 Declare
11 Poetaster
12 Exasperate
13 Communicate
15 High note
16 Peer Gynt's mother
17 Written letter
18 Wedded
20 Chance
21 Lincoln's early love
22 Simon —
23 — Osmond
26 Error
27 College in N.C.
28 Apiece
29 Wine cup
30 Connection
34 Father of Kish
35 Success
36 Small crow
37 Son of Poseidon
39 Foreshadow
40 Motionless
41 Compulsion
42 Hit it off
43 Legal document

DOWN

1 Seraglio
2 Spanish province
3 Tooth
4 Dread
5 Gone aloft
6 Mimicked
7 Elec. unit
8 Extend an arm
9 Back payments
14 Brave's shelter
16 Senior (Fr.)
19 Joan Crawford film
22 Disjoin
23 Signified
24 Spanish seaport
25 Bellowing
26 Church season
28 Grosse —, Mich.
30 Task
31 Venerate
32 Obtain by begging
33 Wool fabric
38 Thrice (Lat.)
39 Abbott

168

PUZZLE 143

ACROSS

1 Infant
5 Tennis great
9 Black
10 Tailor's need
12 Abundant
13 Boob tube
14 Equal (comb. form)
15 Turmeric
16 Uncle (dial.)
17 Notched, as a saw
19 Gain
20 Enclosure
21 Women's rights pioneer
22 Deceive
24 American bird
25 Mexican city
26 Intellect
27 Santa's helper
28 Woman's cloak
31 Pie — mode
32 New Guinea town
33 Pallid
34 Spring-like
36 Deer
37 Hatred
38 "Beetle Bailey" dog
39 Italian city
40 Defrost

DOWN

1 "— Godounoff"
2 Sambuca flavoring
3 Using violence
4 English river
5 Onward
6 Get it?
7 Argue
8 Hermit
10 Soak
11 Taken care of
15 Brawl
18 Horse
21 Small (pref.)
22 Split
23 Greek
24 Despicable
26 Like grain
28 Denture
29 Yule visitor
30 Provide
35 Insect
36 Fiery

169

PUZZLE 144

ACROSS
1 Placed
5 Before stereo
9 Hautboy
10 Distaff title
12 Phonetic term
13 Gaffers
14 Immovable
16 Porker
17 Turkish title
18 Celtic deity
19 Small bottle
22 Dole out
23 Thorax
24 Partake of
25 Run
26 Malediction
27 Go wrong
28 Angelo or Antonio
29 Wood core
30 Doorway part
35 Head ornaments
37 Likewise
38 Being
39 Mediocre
40 Hackman
41 Find out

DOWN
1 Songstress Falana
2 Resting
3 Hebrides island
4 Consider
5 Resembling beer
6 Singular
7 Anonymous
8 Egg specialty
10 French painter
11 Menu item
15 Aid
19 Delightful
20 Impart fresh vigor to
21 Function
22 Disfeature
23 Invent
24 Albacore, e.g.
26 Ex N.Y. governor
28 Condition
31 Ogden —
32 Wild plum
33 Bones (Lat.)
34 Wasteland
36 — Tin Tin

PUZZLE 145

ACROSS
1 Land between two rivers
5 Coarse file
9 To go (Fr.)
11 Single
13 The "V" in VCR
14 Cubic meter
15 — been taken!
16 Importune
18 Defensible
20 Summit
21 Grazing ground
22 Soccer great
23 Delaware city
26 Chinese province
27 Herculean
28 Jordanian mountain
29 Write
30 Restoration
34 Former
36 Palm leaf
37 Signet
38 Melee
40 Finnish lake
41 Savoriness
42 Lady Jane —
43 Undress

DOWN
1 Boat hoist
2 Martini floater
3 Standish's rival
4 Notion
5 Charlotte or Ballet
6 Opposed to
7 Make pleasant
8 Arbor
10 Thief
12 Become profound
17 Old note
19 Seafood sauce
22 Skin opening
23 Testify
24 Aperture
25 Dressing ingredient
26 So help me!
28 Chemise border
30 Bendix TV role
31 Not as good
32 Winged
33 Tailoring feature
35 Fatigue
39 Top off

171

PUZZLE 146

ACROSS
1 Subdue
5 Went by car
9 Loved one
10 Feel remorse
12 Pastry
13 Within
14 Yoko —
15 Dracula's form
16 In favor
17 Mystery writer
19 Wrath
20 Useless fragment
21 Outdo
22 Pulverize
25 Racine drama
26 Come-on
27 Chinese pagoda
28 Work unit
29 Crease
33 Peer Gynt's mother
34 Anc. Heb. measure
35 Veto
36 Poem
38 Jargon
39 Repeat performance
40 Asseverate
41 Circular motion
42 Rockfish

DOWN
1 Russian cosmonaut
2 Turkish city
3 Low I.Q. holder
4 Porker
5 French annuity
6 Jupiter's mother
7 Worshiped as a god
8 Stand behind
10 In good spirits
11 Cylindrical
15 Avian
18 Cooked
21 Frijole
22 Gratify
23 "They're playing —"
24 Importance
25 Principal
27 Overused
29 In what place?
30 Blackguard
31 Cambric, e.g.
32 Surplus
37 And not
38 Auto

172

PUZZLE 147

ACROSS

1 Bistro
5 Theater box
9 Violin maker
11 Actor Jeremy
13 Italian city
14 American actor
15 Slippery customer
16 German article
18 English river
19 French river
21 Thrice (Lat.)
22 Deride
23 Shoot upward
24 With — breath
25 Southpaw
26 Whit
27 Hat or race
28 Lacerate
29 Get started
30 Indian cymbals
31 Permit
32 Function
35 Russian stockade
37 Boredom
39 Sum up
40 Jockey
41 Notch
42 Italian city

DOWN

1 Arrived
2 Lady Friend (Fr.)
3 Come together
4 Greek letter
5 Cuba —
6 Spaniard's gold
7 Leave the beaten path
8 Prayer
10 Verily!
12 Wine type
17 Go wrong
20 Appear
22 Glutted
23 Spanish painter
24 Give and take
25 A,B, or C
27 Billy — Williams
29 Caught
40 winks
33 Fat
34 Ireland
36 Sylvan deity
38 Never (Ger.)

173

PUZZLE 148

ACROSS
1 Example
5 Son of Jacob
10 Overhead
12 Lady's
   garment
13 Actress
   Ruth
14 Mortal
15 Poem
16 Convivial
18 Summer (Fr.)
19 Paul
   or Edwin
21 Signature
   (abbr.)
22 "— the
   Horrible"
24 Lackaday!
25 Greek
   island
27 Correct
29 Celtic deity
30 Bequest
   recipient
32 Expert
33 Cole —
36 O'Neill
   drama
37 Bulgarian
   coin
38 Hasten
39 Islamic
   title
41 Wear away
43 Old
   chariot
44 Frosted

45 Feats
46 Ethereal

DOWN
1 "Gigi" star
2 Dwelling
3 Not here
4 Woman's
   name
5 Pallid

6 Man's
   nickname
7 One's
   dwelling
8 Euphoria
9 Quit a
   bargain
11 Thinking
   marriage

17 Anecdotal
   collection
20 Flooring
   item
23 Overflowed
25 Alleged
26 Solitu-
   dinarian

28 Sea (Fr.)
31 Unclose
   (poet.)
34 Duck
35 Frail
37 Striplings
40 Guided
42 Inlet

174

PUZZLE 149

ACROSS

1 Procreate
6 Greek island
11 Breathing
12 Dress fabric
13 Glandular organ
14 Appraised
15 New Guinea town
16 Scottish explorer
18 Swiss canton
19 Informed
21 Elec. unit
22 Legislate
23 Egyptian king
24 Love (It.)
25 Priest's vestment
26 Mature
27 Earl "—" Hines
28 Black cuckoo
29 De Luise film
30 Vereen
31 N.Y. city
32 Where (Lat.)
35 English architect, — Jones
37 Blustered
39 Scurry off
40 Mrs. R.F.K.
41 Extra inning
42 Shabby

DOWN

1 Good time
2 Charles Lamb
3 Opine
4 Night before
5 Balcony
6 Fallen rock
7 Altar constellation
8 Wise thinking
9 "The Gypsy Baron," e.g.
10 Chancel seats
17 Skill
20 Merchandise
22 High position
23 Drunkards
24 Near East expert
25 Party supplier
27 Actress Wray
29 Foam
33 Vegetable
34 Without working
36 "I've — Rhythm"
38 One — time

PUZZLE 150

ACROSS

1 Dismiss
5 Radiation device
10 So. African plant
11 Get lost!
12 Roman historian
13 Alaskans
14 Summer (Fr.)
15 "Where the Boys—"
16 However (var.)
17 Mixture
19 Judah Ben—
20 Peggy of song
21 Trial run
22 Kitchen device
25 Isaac or Helen
26 Baccha-nals' cry
27 Fervid
28 Man's nickname
29 "Citizen Kane" sled
33 Jeanne d'—
34 Night before
35 United
36 Stab
38 Hairdo
39 Old movie
40 Before (Lat.)
41 Impediment (Law)
42 Gaze

DOWN

1 Oregon city
2 Choice part
3 Original
4 TV actress Susan—
5 Free-for-all
6 Generation
7 Poet Laureate (1813-43)
8 Carry on over
9 Holiday places
11 Freight boat
15 City of Manasseh
18 Toward shelter
21 Poet Allen—
22 Reversion
23 The piano (sl.)
24 Musical event
25 Stockings
27 Mean dwelling
29 Sum up
30 Kentucky pioneer
31 Confed-erate
32 Postpone
37 River (Sp.)
38 Top off

PUZZLE 151

ACROSS
1 Leafy fare
6 Niggard
11 Each
12 Finnish lake
13 Loaded
14 Make tardy
15 Kadota, e.g.
16 Fuss
18 Wood core
19 Minimize
21 Dress, as stone
22 Consumed
23 Insect
24 "Vanity Fair" heroine
27 Accelerated
28 She (Fr.)
29 Cap
30 Daisy — Scraggs
31 Naval might
34 Japanese verse
35 Bird's beak
36 Whole
38 Biblical mount
40 Embankment
42 Happening
43 The best
44 Libyan city
45 Burghoff TV role

DOWN
1 Psyche
2 Assistance
3 Shelf
4 Verb form
5 Joan Collins TV program
6 Casaba, e.g.
7 Actress Balin
8 Diabolical
9 Hermit
10 Backed out
17 Scottish river
20 Ginza drink
23 "Pistol-Packin' —"
24 Abstracted
25 Superlative in grammar
26 Detergent
27 Gadabout
29 "Three" in Udine
31 "West Side Story" role
32 He killed Goliath
33 Prince Valiant's wife
37 Sly gaze
39 Girl's name
41 Old note

PUZZLE 152

ACROSS
1 Somber
5 Assail
10 Have no more
11 Tranquil
12 Algerian city
13 Card suit
14 "Wow, it's brisk!"
15 Barrel
16 Old hand
17 Fire's remains
19 Author Levin
20 WWI hero
21 Highlander
22 Thrust
24 N.H. city
25 Spur on
26 Athletic group
27 Spanish article
28 Ancient Greece
30 Beverage
31 Consume
32 Untried
34 Biblical woman
36 Germanic letter
37 Overrun
38 Facility
39 Badly off
40 Absconded

DOWN
1 Lump
2 "M" star
3 Soldiers on standby
4 Pop and Junior
5 Vegetables
6 Age
7 Product literature
8 Begin
9 Leaving a valid will
11 Great white —
15 Same
18 Impure diamond
21 Otarian
22 Role for Richard Boone
23 Mollusk
24 Gael
26 Tantalize
28 Intoxicating
29 Feel
33 Tobacco (sl.)
35 Rapscallion
36 Ring arbiter

PUZZLE 153

ACROSS

1 Wynter
  or Andrews
5 Jacob's
  son
10 Type face
12 Fissile rock
13 The old
  man's mate
15 Celtic
  deity
16 —
  standstill
17 Native of
  (suff.)
18 Caprice
20 Drinking
  vessel
21 Staying
  place
22 Split
23 Salt water
26 Chopped,
  as carrots
27 Rockfish
28 Fiery
29 Choose
30 Inhabit
33 Metric
  measure
34 Memorable
  time
35 Scope
37 Family
  gathering
  place
40 German city

41 Wear
  away
42 In want
43 Encourage

DOWN

1 Valley
2 Sci-fi film
3 Explosive
4 Lawyer
  (abbr.)
5 Egyptian
  city

6 Japanese
  measure
7 Of Ham's
  descendant
8 Superlative
  in grammar
9 Backed out
11 Arthurian
  lady
14 Jacket
  style

19 Actress
  Louise
22 Donizetti
  opera
23 Expand
24 Musical
  repetition
25 Vivid
26 Contribute
28 Title in
  Austria

30 Itsy
  -bitsy
31 Powerful
  one
32 Diacritical
  mark
36 Get
  together
38 Man's
  nickname
39 Macaw

179

PUZZLE 154

ACROSS
1 Asian country
5 Cavil
9 Canyon mouth
10 White poplar
12 Manifest
15 Hardened
16 One — time
17 Golf term
18 Japanese coin
19 Rabbit fur
22 Annulet
23 French patron saint
24 Horse
25 Evaluate
26 Stay clear of
27 Before
28 Gazzara
29 Lesley — Warren
30 Football pass
35 Idea
37 Hoist
38 Deep mud
39 Czech river
40 Winglike

DOWN
1 Sweet-heart
2 Urge on
3 Heraldic wreath
4 Unscathed
5 Collapse, as a mine
6 Tolerate
7 Ruby
8 Comely
11 — Cordiale
13 Havelock —
14 Dance
19 Pupil
20 Lobster's feelers
21 Baked treat
22 Disen-cumber
23 Fantasy
24 Producer Carlo
26 Las Vegas employee
28 World-weary
31 Jane Austen novel
32 Speak harshly
33 Indian city
34 Unfriendly look
36 Drinking vessel

180

PUZZLE 155

ACROSS

1 Give up
5 Adorn with jewels
10 Paddled
12 An Astaire
13 Nimble-footed
14 All inclusive
15 Bulgarian coin
16 College in Iowa
18 Greenland Eskimo
19 Bounty hunter's earning
21 Anais —
22 Zola novel
23 Chinese factory
24 Impudence (sl.)
26 Trace
27 Finn
28 Horse
29 Brazilian tree
30 Newest
32 Handle clumsily
33 Destiny
34 Amateur radio
36 Silver (Sp.)
38 Rent
40 Scott heroine
41 Upper crust
42 Viking leader
43 Be peevish

DOWN

1 Fuel
2 Avid
3 Made cuckoo
4 Moray
5 With — breath
6 Taro root
7 Miff
8 Making ecstatic
9 Potpourri
11 Pour carefully
17 Hour (Ital.)
20 Insect
23 Employ
24 Bell's tongue
25 Italian seaport
26 Blab
28 Chairman —
30 Plain (Sp.)
31 Savor
35 Convene
37 — Aviv
39 Sprite

181

PUZZLE 156

ACROSS
1 Fall short
5 Lance
10 Sicilian city
11 Don't kid me!
13 Before (Lat.)
14 Intention
15 Stadium cheer
16 Insect
17 Frances or Sandra
18 Actor Jannings
20 Swiss city
21 Bring out
22 A Kennedy
23 Choice
24 Gaffe
25 Fearing that
26 Intimidated
27 Vaudeville features
28 Actor Conried
29 School group
30 Rested
31 Thrice (Lat.)
34 Wicked
36 Prima donna
37 Sheathe
38 Augury
39 Ascertain
40 Pavilion

DOWN
1 Trepidation
2 "— Lucasta"
3 Far off
4 New Guinea town
5 Figure of speech
6 Scheme
7 Porker
8 Tolerate; endure
9 Backward
12 Youngster
16 French resort
19 Pooches
20 Helen Gurley —
21 Choosing
23 Run its course
24 Vessel
26 Swiss house
30 Iranian city
32 Divisible by two
33 Bombast
35 — chance!
36 Speck

PUZZLE 157

ACROSS

1 Ready money
5 In a line
9 Run
10 Greek island
12 Russian city
13 Games
15 Japanese verse
16 Permit
17 Retreat
18 Do battle with
20 That's how!
21 Step—!
22 Bird of peace
23 Suit piece
25 Allude
26 Norse sea god
27 Irish playwright
28 Church part
29 Flowers
32 Actor Alastair
33 Noah's son
34 Drink
35 Isolate
37 —fixe
38 Register
39 Curia tribunal
40 Clothes
41 Swedish wine measure

DOWN

1 Whack
2 Main artery
3 Give an opinion
4 Child of Loki
5 Concurrence
6 Engrossed
7 Shoulder (prefix)
8 Sage advice
11 Ship's derrick
14 Snigger
16 "Hi and —"
19 Between (Fr.)
20 Perfect
23 Aspect
24 Lofty
25 Baba au —
27 Bullocks
30 Michelangelo work
31 Trident, e.g.
33 Toboggan
36 Man's nickname
37 Irish rebel group

PUZZLE 158

ACROSS

1 Midst
5 Title holder
10 Solitary
11 Account
13 Resiliency
14 Dinner item
15 Gold (Sp.)
16 — and Fox
17 Dutch commune
18 Overused
20 Rowan of comedy
21 Conveying device
22 Simple
23 Luster
24 Bad bettor
25 They egg roosters on
26 Lukewarm
27 Work unit
28 Transport agent
29 Sandy's bark
30 Yes (Fr.)
31 Simpleton
34 Implanting tesserae
36 Competent
37 Fireplace
38 Hint
39 Corset pieces
40 Caution

DOWN

1 Counter-tenor
2 Anchor
3 Just like that
4 Failing grade
5 Come up with
6 Therefore
7 Likely
8 A better deal
9 Ready to serve
12 High-schooler
16 Location
19 Diamond scores
21 Queen Annes, e.g
22 Be gloomy
23 Casing
24 Jacob's son
26 Bruisers
28 Funny Python
32 Swing about
33 Progeny
35 Irish rebel group
36 Alas!

PUZZLE 159

ACROSS

1 Greek mountain
5 "Patton" star
10 Sullen
11 Shaping machines
13 American playwright
14 Stellar
15 Droop
16 Pompey's greeting
17 Japanese river
18 Plaited
20 Punster
21 Germ
22 Make the scene
23 Biblical juniper tree
25 Musical style
26 Arab official
27 Bench
28 — Tse-tung
29 Gonfalon
32 Hostelry
33 Play a role
34 Judah Ben —
35 Texas river
37 Deep mud
38 Accumulated
39 Vase handle
40 Banish
41 Editor's mark

DOWN

1 Poet
2 Sub's device
3 Office fixture
4 Metric measure
5 Overworked
6 Boxed
7 Baseball great
8 Give a reminder
9 When to pour
12 Candidate lists
16 Ancient gold alloy
19 Prophet
22 Group of families
23 Negligent
24 Spring forth
25 Crooked
27 Break with
29 Jury list
30 Care for
31 Handle
36 Son of Bela
37 Barker and Perkins

185

PUZZLE 160

ACROSS

1 So. Afr. fox
5 Child of Loki
8 Gait
9 Malt vinegar
13 Icelandic measure
14 Restore
15 So (Lat.)
16 Soak
17 Nest
18 At a low pitch
20 Move restlessly
21 Crocus
22 Boundary
23 Shallow container
25 "Sunflower" star
26 She (Fr.)
27 Coarse file
28 Brazilian tree
29 Undergarment
31 Sib
32 Writer Serling
33 Nigerian
35 Football term
37 Strikebreaker

38 Inhabit
39 "Beautiful —"
40 Actress Susan
41 English river

DOWN

1 Woe is me!

2 Compact
3 The Moluccas
4 Poetical adverb
5 Man's name
6 Sad verse
7 Bulgarian coin

10 Just dandy!
11 Fly
12 Blush
16 Whirl
19 Pa. city
22 A Hart
23 Large cup
24 Lofty
25 Fat

27 Andy Hardy portrayer
29 Unrefined
30 Get in shape
34 Hautboy
36 Get — of
37 Tippler

186

PUZZLE 161

ACROSS
1 Cooking herb
5 Spore case
10 Czech river
11 Chronology
13 Ceremony
14 Off the ship
15 Wallach
16 Incorrectly (pref.)
17 French article
18 Sword-shaped
20 Hipster
21 Czech religious reformer
22 Vidal book
23 Jesting
25 Dictatorial
26 Commedia dell' —
27 Move swiftly
28 "How, Now — Jones?"
29 Small fish
31 Marsh elder
32 Neronian greeting
33 Swab
35 Bristly
37 In our presence
38 Actress Claire
39 Gaelic
40 Actor George
41 Belgian river

DOWN
1 Dried up
2 Sprightly
3 Find trouble
4 Before
5 Characteristics
6 German writer
7 Plane formation (abbr.)
8 Un-flappable ones
9 In — (defaulting)
12 "— Rides Again"
16 Pole
19 Unfaltering
22 By nature
23 Cruel one
24 Maxim
25 Curse
27 Amuse
29 "Lolita" star
30 Not improving
34 Equal
36 Where (It.)
37 Hold it!

PUZZLE 162

ACROSS

1 Engrossed
5 Florida city
10 Grecian theaters
11 Moniker
12 European river
13 Au courant
15 Sea eagle
16 Two make a tenner
17 Denial
18 Utilizing
20 Cratchit child
21 Bit by a bee
22 Dad or Junior
23 Wise ones
24 Mature
25 Rose derivative
26 Damp
27 Nothing
28 Physician (sl.)
29 Indian cymbals
30 Beverage
31 Such (Fr.)
34 Contented
36 Hungarian dog breed
37 Of a Great Lake
38 Gaelic
39 Mideast country
40 Adolescent

DOWN

1 Abie's Irish —
2 Hebrew month
3 Theater section (sl.)
4 Road covering
5 Domesticating
6 Lengthwise
7 Amongst
8 Express artistically
9 Beset
14 God of marriage
16 Saw bucks
19 Litigious one
21 Gluts
22 "La Bohème" heroine
23 Yule visitor
24 Boorish
26 Montana city
28 African tribe
32 Different
33 Claim
35 Ventilate
36 Favorite

PUZZLE 163

ACROSS
1 Instance
5 Pontifical
10 Exclude
11 Raucous
12 Distance
13 Printing gaffes
14 Anglo-Saxon king
15 Little Margaret
16 Molecule
17 One of the reel Bonds, really
19 Hit sign
20 Expense
21 Saddle strap
22 Tax
23 — Hari
24 Ness
25 Ham's son
26 Lubricate
27 Actress Ann
30 Mining discovery
31 Egyptian king
32 Law (Fr.)
33 Jump
35 Tipster
36 Author Gunther's word
37 Gaelic
38 Itsy-bitsy
40 German river

DOWN
1 Ludicrous
2 — acid
3 Library wall sign
4 Summer, in Macon
5 Fish type
6 Swiss river
7 Prayer meeting phrase
8 Oregon city
9 Strong-arm
11 Compassion
15 Botch
18 — out (defeat)
21 Imprudent
22 Of Egypt's capital
23 Pooch
24 Stop fighting!
25 Auto style
27 Ponder
28 Excite
29 Saltpeter
34 Fraternity emblem
35 Duffer's gadget

189

PUZZLE 164

ACROSS

1 Fasten
6 Elapsed
10 Throw
11 Basic precept
13 Peruvian
14 Cattle spread
15 "To Helen" poet
16 Goddess (Lat.)
18 Hockey great
19 — public
21 Uncle (Sp.)
22 Number of Muses
23 Subsequently
24 Exhausted
26 "Well-groomed" woman?
27 Sell for
28 — in (restrain)
29 Tree
30 Soviet lake
32 Recent (prefix)
33 Unseal (poet.)
34 Untruth
36 Register
38 "— Triste"
40 Accumulate
41 Senseless
42 Irish island
43 Liquid measure

DOWN

1 Expedite
2 It fits the mortise
3 Be in a hurry
4 Burma's old name
5 Jewelry piece
6 Meander
7 Grazing ground
8 Instantly
9 Denounced
12 Royal seat
17 Before
20 Color
23 Concert group
24 Views
25 Italian corn meal delicacy
26 Torment
28 Ghost sound
30 "El Cid" star
31 French river
35 Kind of garden
37 Time period
39 Black cuckoo

PUZZLE 165

ACROSS

1 Yearn
5 Pierce
9 African lake
10 Greek poet
12 Infrequent
13 Sold
15 Aim
16 Tibetan gazelle
17 Growl
18 Manifest
20 Bikini part
21 Fancy wear
23 Ooze out
24 Within (pref.)
25 Annoy
26 Reverberate
27 Maiden efforts
28 Pronoun
29 Start doing
30 Cravat
31 Dutch commune
32 Yellow bugle
35 Whoever chooses to
37 From a distance
38 Progress
39 Reddish color
40 Chalcedony
41 Olive genus

DOWN

1 Israeli port
2 Toler film role
3 Ugly (sl.)
4 Nigerian city
5 Palatable
6 Delight
7 French river
8 "Pumping iron" goal
11 Most approachable
14 Window embellishments
16 German city
19 — Beach, Fla.
21 Fun time in Tabasco
22 Moving by degrees
23 Ham's grandson
25 Head (Fr.)
27 Rely
29 Title in Tampico
33 Urn
34 Greek river
36 Japanese river
37 Nigerian

PUZZLE 166

ACROSS

1 Famous musical
5 Less hazardous
10 Forearm bone
11 Moses or Dorothy
12 Aspect
13 Wards off
14 Soft food
15 Ready
16 Beach
18 Initiated (poet.)
19 Before
20 Hundred (Fr.)
21 Niggard
24 Thespian lists
25 Single
26 Good (Fr.)
27 Salt (Fr.)
28 Unpretentious
31 Roman officer
33 Cut down
35 Comfy
36 Zola novel
37 Washed
38 Adamant
39 Outmoded
40 Sprightly

DOWN

1 Lug; tote
2 Assumed name
3 Unskillful
4 Managed
5 Rescued
6 Syrian city
7 Searches for food
8 Contest joiner
9 Takes umbrage at
11 French river
15 Young salmon
17 Whirl
20 Walking —
21 Frank's condiment
22 Idolence
23 Important
24 Signaling system
26 Made into fillets
28 Pondered
29 Take part in
30 Vickers or Mauro
32 Pedestal
34 Lack
36 Wee drink

192

PUZZLE 167

ACROSS

1 Hurt
5 Increased
9 Afrikaan
10 Withstand
13 Joie de vivre
14 Holy day
15 Hebrew letter
16 Foundation
17 Giggling sound
18 Black
20 Malayan coin
21 Barracks sound
22 Man's nickname
23 Georgia city
24 Sanctify
25 Winglike
26 Wild shot
27 Mortal or venial
28 Crete's capital
29 Stitch
30 Antique
31 Dweller in (suffix)
34 Empower
36 Cut
37 Recipe direction
38 Raison d' —
39 African river
40 So that's how!

DOWN

1 Encourage
2 Soft drink flavor
3 Lubitsch film (1943)
4 Sea eagle
5 British novelist
6 Prepare
7 Written letter
8 In heaven
11 Distaff prophet
12 Unexpected pleasures
16 By nature
19 Vulgarian
21 Obvious
22 Shropshire hills
23 The — (hoi polloi)
24 German club
26 Kansas city
28 Bobwhite
32 Exhaust
33 Fencing foil
35 Bikini part
36 Six (Ital.)

193

PUZZLE 168

ACROSS
1 Fruit or Waldorf
6 Blemish
10 Awakened
11 Preminger film
13 Pens
14 "Maltese Falcon" co-star
15 Dutch cupboard
16 Marine bird
18 Unshut (poet.)
19 Otate
21 Keel part
22 Twaddled
24 Out of whack
25 Adjust again
26 Spanish pineapples
27 "Good Earth" heroine
28 Dionysus' mother
29 Peruke
30 Musical sounds
31 Papal name
32 Panty-hose's curse
33 Cut down
36 Elicit
38 Straighten
40 Pine derivative
41 For the —
42 Imprint
43 — over (endured)

DOWN
1 Pillage
2 Venezuelan copper center
3 Limber, as a dishrag
4 Snake
5 1849 Mormon state
6 Vapid
7 Spanish article
8 Distraught
9 Balmy
12 Sandy
17 Scarlet
20 Egyptian solar disk
22 Sneak thief
23 Soothed
24 Fruit
26 Banner
28 — markee
30 English river
34 Formerly
35 Tobacco (sl.)
37 Sib
39 Law (Fr.)

194

PUZZLE 169

ACROSS

1 Lorre role
5 Faction
9 Viva voce
10 Posthaste
13 South-
   western
   lawman
15 Actor
   Wallach
16 Waterfall
   (Scot.)
17 Communist
18 In good
   shape
19 Queen
   in India
20 Quarrel
23 Author
   Hunter
24 War deity
25 Star in Lyra
26 For fear
   that
27 Emblem
   of victory
29 Elec. units
30 "Chances
   —"
31 Menagerie
32 Japanese
   measure
33 Enemy
36 Famed
   marks-
   woman
39 Slice
   of bacon
40 Alleviate
41 Sea eagle
42 Colored

DOWN

1 Dust
   particle
2 Russian
   city
3 Hirsch
   TV show
4 Palm leaf
5 Pixie
6 Mideast
   country
7 Russian
   river
8 Intaglio
   creator
11 Adolescent
12 First,
   third, e.g.
14 Pier
18 Food
   restraints
19 Musical
   show
20 Portuguese
   statesman
21 Italian city
22 Reaction
27 City in
   Pakistan
28 Venezuelan
   copper
   center
32 Espied
33 Crit-
   icize
34 Bacteri-
   ologist's
   wire
35 Watched
37 You
   (Ger.)
38 Sheep
   tick

PUZZLE 170

ACROSS
1 Roman statesman
5 Companion of 'earty
8 Base
9 German uhlan
13 Involved with
14 Indian city
15 Woman's nickname
16 Pagoda ornament
17 Swab
18 Reclines
20 Greek letter
21 Restraints
23 Icelandic measure
24 Italian city
25 Strainer
26 She (Fr.)
27 Classified
28 Muslim name
29 Succinct
30 Catnip
31 Edible root
32 Word with leaf
35 Sword-shaped
37 Indigent
38 Whirled
39 Bulwer Lytton heroine
40 Soul (Fr.)
41 Free scope

DOWN
1 Crosspatch
2 The best
3 Sky phe-nomenon
4 Sioux
5 Non-citizens
6 Racers places
7 Finis
10 Perfect ninny
11 Caustic
12 Com-plained
16 Accept
19 "— homo"
21 Household product
22 A Greek
23 Put on —
25 Rail bird
27 Bolt
29 Indian symbol
33 Scottish island
34 Lady Jane—
36 Wing (Lat.)
37 Dilly

196

PUZZLE 171

ACROSS
1 Garment
5 Excursion
9 Streamlet
10 Compassion
12 "—Bede"
13 Penniless
15 Scottish name prefix
16 Metric measure
17 Lift cage
18 Lyric poem
20 Japanese statesman
21 Gray matter
23 Invent
24 Embankment
25 Feather
26 Coup d'—
27 Unfastened
28 Be ill
29 In Dixie
30 Vineyard (Fr.)
31 Garfield, e.g.
32 Old note
35 Tilted
37 Filament
38 "Lorna—"
39 Adamant
40 Penury
41 Sicilian volcano

DOWN
1 Stuff, as a suitcase
2 Verdi opera
3 Assess
4 Tree
5 Degree, rail and base
6 —Adoree
7 Actor Carmichael
8 Term of endearment
11 British ritual
14 Hummed
16 First-rate
19 Magpie
21 Whiten
22 On pension
23 Coagulate
25 Sulk
27 Packed
29 Setting
33 Celebrity
34 Indian buffalo
36 Love (Scot.)
37 Hasten

197

PUZZLE 172

ACROSS
1 Boundary
5 Unharmed
9 Venerate
11 Forward
13 Spur part
14 Amalgamate
15 Wing (Lat.)
16 Cry of surprise
18 Fetched
19 Saltpeter
21 Table scrap
22 Infuriate
24 Theater box
25 Construe
26 Jockey
27 Portico
28 Leafy dishes
29 Indian weight
30 Wore
31 Fruit beverage
32 Man's name
33 Drop in price
36 Vichy premier
38 Ghost
40 Stone pillar
41 Punctures
42 Colleen's name
43 Land map

DOWN
1 "Doctor Zhivago" role
2 Graven image
3 For good
4 Before
5 Philippine island
6 Beverage
7 From now on
8 Overfilled
10 Click beetle
12 Achievers
17 Biddy
20 Concept
22 Mass books
23 Precede
24 French songstress
26 Vegetable
28 — ammoniac
30 Troy name
34 Thought
35 Nuisance
37 Muslim name
37 Muslim name
39 Short flight

198

PUZZLE 173

ACROSS

1 Venezuelan copper center
5 Surmount
8 Cantinflas film
9 Visigoth king
13 Athena's title
14 "Porgy and Bess" role
15 Give the ax to
16 Title
17 Burro
18 Urgent
20 Drop the bait
21 Please, not that!
22 Malediction
23 "— Love Song"
25 Earth worker
26 Church season
27 Twine
28 Swiss canton
29 Ideological rivalry
32 Tease
33 Eggs (Lat.)
34 Brown kiwi
35 Not out
37 Sinewy
38 Communication
39 Preminger
40 Baseball great
41 Withdraw

DOWN

1 Swiftly
2 Ease up
3 Thespian's thrill
4 Candlenut tree fiber
5 Las Vegas place
6 Open-eyed
7 Average
10 Be literate
11 Deranged
12 Wyoming city
16 Alpine herdsman
19 Ruminant
22 Celtic star
23 More than one
24 Make effervescent
25 Tropical sunfish
27 Furtive
29 One of Santa's reindeer
30 Main artery
31 Man-made fabric
36 Sioux
37 Holy Toledo!

PUZZLE 174

ACROSS

1 Milton poem
6 Body of worshipers
10 Vexed
11 Violently
13 Ticket collector
14 Montana city
15 Summer, in Nancy
16 —d' Aosta, Italy
18 Palance film
19 Get away
21 Concealed
22 Resiliency
23 Vinous
24 Man's nickname
25 "Turandot" character
26 Lean-to
27 Cadence
28 Owns
29 Boil
31 Killer whale
32 Network
33 Within (comb. form)
35 Greek letter
37 Humble
39 Drift
40 Locality
41 Interpret
42 Inscriptions on coins

DOWN

1 Quote
2 Get on a soapbox
3 Gets there
4 Colorado Indian
5 Domestic
6 Fur
7 Aussie's bird
8 Nab doing
9 Giving a tenth
12 In want
17 Go — over
20 Campus beauty
23 A Chamberlain
24 Word after snake
25 Parti-colored horse
26 —full of holes
27 Trevino of golf
29 Turf
30 Follow
34 Kinski film role
36 Tibetan gazelle
38 Feather scarf

PUZZLE 175

ACROSS

1 Back of the neck
5 Social stratum
10 Pa. city
11 Fine fur
12 Musical event
14 I love (Lat.)
15 Senorita's "gold"
16 Greek nickname
17 Cossack leader
19 Debussy's "La—"
20 Distant (comb. form)
21 Smooth consonant
22 Photo
24 Bare
25 Cut to bits
26 Pullet
27 Spanish article
28 Infrequently
31 Cunning
32 Favoring
33 Young Saluki
35 Tasty sandwich
38 College official
39 Spoken
40 Adversary
41 Gloomy aura

DOWN

1 Italian river
2 Redolence
3 Embroidery loop
4 Horrors!
5 Church regulation
6 Jeanne d'—
7 Ship
8 Earthly
9 Unabridged
11 Virtuous
13 Heavenly sight
18 On
21 Afford
22 Curtail
23 Kidnapper's pawn
24 Cranshaw, e.g
25 Actress Ina
26 Afghan city
28 Thorny
29 La Scala's specialty
30 Wall painting
34 Vox populi sampling
36 Man's nickname
37 Bounce

201

PUZZLE 176

ACROSS
1 Gab
5 Wrongly
10 Individual
11 Right now!
12 Angel (Fr.)
13 Heavy
14 Helios
15 Contrived
16 David's officer
17 Come before
19 Townsman
20 O'Neill play
21 Tissue
22 Bactrian, e.g.
25 Affectations
26 Not— (not at all)
27 Pronoun
28 French dance
29 Skunk
33 Beverage
34 Epoch
35 Moslem potentate
36 Meandered
38 Twofold
39 Turbine
40 Concerning
41 Adolescent years
42 Acute

DOWN
1 Embrace
2 Integrity
3 Point of view
4 Duffer's need
5 Mountain crest
6 Extinct N.Z. bird
7 Reference lists
8 Barren
9 Musical compositions
11 "Tabled" item
15 Grow wearisome
18 Parliament
21 Lacerated
22 Minnelli film
23 Delicious mollusk
24 Space traveled
25 Chinese wax
27 Throng
29 Hammer parts
30 Justification
31 Playing marble
32 Claw
37 Chinese river
38 Mail, in India

PUZZLE 177

ACROSS

1 Author Bellow
5 Maxim
8 Underseas plant
9 Thespian
13 Hawaiian chant
14 Treat sumptuously
15 Jazz great, Kid —
16 Smite
17 Variant of Anne
18 Strength
20 Small violin
21 Disappear
22 Actress Rowlands
23 Apex
25 Lobster trap
26 Israeli dance
27 Nixon staffer
28 "— was going to St. Ives"
29 Italian pastry
32 Get 'em, Fido!
33 Slower (mus.)
34 Biddy
35 Becharm
37 Tennis term
38 Froglike
39 Arab official
40 Guided
41 Charter

DOWN

1 Greek island
2 On guard
3 Brando in "The —"
4 New Guinea town
5 Race
6 Prince Valiant's wife
7 Humorist
10 Anti-American shout
11 Astolat maid
12 Type of library
16 Part of Excalibur
19 Arizona city
22 Smirk
23 Bar order
24 Count Almaviva's love
25 Jargon
27 Word after white or gray
29 Beldam
30 "Death-trap" playwright
31 Sluggish
36 Wire measure
37 Celtic deity

203

PUZZLE 178

ACROSS
1 Resource
6 Spur part
11 Kitchen gadget
12 Silly
13 Finnish lake
14 Blend
15 Father of Kish
16 Mimic
18 And not
19 Piercing tool
20 Performed
21 Son of Bela
22 Fitzgerald
24 Angel (Fr.)
25 Ade book
27 Detroit player
28 Vale
29 Vend
30 Top card
31 Disfeature
32 Simpleton
35 Cosset
36 Tune
37 Whack
38 Giant
40 White poplar
42 Happening
43 Opera great, Emma —
44 Libyan city
45 Ford name

DOWN
1 Sports ambience
2 Muscle
3 Hawthorne classic
4 Bard's adverb
5 Foot lever
6 Frosted
7 United
8 Found on medicine bottles
9 Overfill
10 More cautious
17 Miss Lindstrom
23 "Diamond —"
24 Trouble
25 Modified
26 Come into
27 House feature
29 Capuchin monkey
31 Devil-fish
33 Soothing cream
34 Metal
39 Woman's name
41 Nasty

204

PUZZLE 179

ACROSS

1 Church part
5 Curvatures
11 Cry
12 Bidding
13 Field
14 Fly
15 You (Ger.)
16 Sault
— Marie
17 Capek
play
18 Tomahawk
20 Color
21 Require
22 History
23 Additional
24 Challenge
25 Head
26 Dress
adornment
27 Plane
formation
(abbr.)
28 Pastry
or pie
31 Vedic
sky
serpent
32 I, in Berlin
33 Gotcha!
34 German
children
36 Canter
37 Hire
38 Spirit
lamp
39 Tyrant
40 Belgian
river

DOWN

1 Stupefy
2 Peninsula
of
Venezuela
3 Words twixt
lovers
4 Old note
5 Subsided
6 Face with
masonry
7 Greek
letter
8 One's
true love
9 Inlet
10 Shandy's
creator
16 Irish
fairies
19 Wax
22 Minus
23 Apparatus
24 Soupcon
25 Lapel
style
26 Arcane
28 Zorro's
real
name
29 European
river
30 Russian
republic
35 Drop
the
bait
36 Whodunit
author

PUZZLE 180

ACROSS

1 Johnny of song
5 Roger Bacon, e.g.
10 — Velez
11 Small ear
13 Suburb of Paris
14 "Streetcar" role
15 Oriental porgy
16 Summer (Fr.)
17 Bo's rating
18 Recorded
20 Chinese dynasty
21 "Last Stand" leader
23 Bacteriologist's wire
24 Tati's "Mon —"
25 Winter drink
26 English poet
27 Illness
28 Perceive
29 Kitten
30 Youngling
31 Man's name
32 Permit
35 Baffled
37 Peace symbol
38 Tell
39 Fixed quantity
40 Exclude
41 Eye action

DOWN

1 Coagulate
2 Atmosphere
3 One type of working shift
4 Hold it!
5 Rot
6 Evaluated
7 Anger
8 Without cease
9 Manumitted
12 Leather shop
16 Fencing foil
19 Salt tree
21 Ship or sled
22 Opened
23 Lubricants
25 Building (Sp.)
27 "Dial M for —"
29 Michelangelo work
33 Devilish
34 Head (Fr.)
36 Tap
37 Couple

PUZZLE 181

ACROSS
1 Hurt
5 Sophisti-
 cated
10 Willing
11 Jeremiad
13 Enthuse
14 Immedi-
 ately
15 Biblical
 lion
16 You (Ger.)
17 O'Neill play
18 Wall
 bracket
20 Owl's cry
21 Fresh
 out of
22 Gaelic
23 Throw
25 Speed
 demon
26 High-
 pitched
 sound
27 Knitting
 stitch
28 Vase
 handle
29 Rose
 essence
31 Wager
32 Generation
33 Adjust
35 Ethically
 weak
37 Bavarian
 river
38 Spanish
 saint

39 Anatomical
 network
40 Lacelike
41 Really now!

DOWN
1 Indian city
2 Her name
 means
 "bright"

3 Reserved
4 Nigerian
 city
5 American
 statesman
6 Recent
7 I love
 (Lat.)
8 Advanced
 students

9 Hem in
12 Wobble
16 Melody
19 Dance
20 — and soul
23 "— Mater"
24 Football
 players
25 Herb
 genus

27 Bet
30 Lasso
32 Orient
34 Card
 player's
 three
36 Inactive
 (abbr.)
37 Son
 of Bela

207

PUZZLE 182

ACROSS

1 Apportioned
6 Brilliant-colored fish
10 Red planet
14 American playwright
19 Carroll heroine
20 Tidal flood
21 Israeli city
22 Lips
23 Charges against
24 Ardor
25 Actor: — Ray
26 Tooth substance
27 Waldorf, for one
28 One of the Caesars
29 White of egg
30 Wisteria, et al.
31 Fragile
34 Shakespeare play
36 Salt, in Paris
39 Arachnid
40 Uncle (dial.)
42 Regan's father
43 Rural sound
46 Divorce allowance
48 Genuflect
50 Blackguards
52 To send back
53 Dutch ophthalmologist
55 Marshy meadows
56 Author Loos
57 Injection
58 Adam's grandson

60 Wrathful
61 Detest
62 Protective ditches
63 Badgerlike animals
65 An affirmative
66 Odor
68 Mine entrances
70 Bone: comb. form
73 Marbles
76 Moderates
78 House, in Spain
82 Word with lock or dance
84 Remainder
85 God of love
86 Cornered
87 American author
89 Mountain in Washington
91 A stream
92 Vinegars made of ale
94 Distinct parts
95 Merge
96 Kind of deer
97 Followers of isms
99 Head of the fairway
100 Male turkeys
101 Variant of 40 Across
102 Moves furtively
104 Transverse stripe
107 Nebraska Indian

110 A form of potter's wheel
112 Thing, in law
113 Wales on the skin
117 Former U.S. Senator
118 Case for small articles
119 "Der — "; Adenauer
120 Philippine timber tree
121 Babylonian hero
122 Serpent lizard
123 Nearly all
124 Roman official
125 Star in Cygnus
126 Very, in France
127 Individuals
128 Repair a lawn

DOWN

1 Small rugs
2 Pseudonym of Charles Lamb
3 Money drawer
4 Outward (Anat.)
5 Wife of Othello
6 Dieter's problem
7 Word with dog or state
8 Plowed land
9 Barnyard creature
10 Repast
11 God of the Moslems
12 Kind of tire
13 One who rages
14 Dickens hero

15 Ship's crane
16 Black
17 Snow or whitewall
18 Utters
29 Coupled
32 "Swedish Nightingale"
33 Dogmas
35 Asian country
36 Miss Bernhardt
37 Turgenev heroine
38 Boundary
41 Lamprey fisherman
43 Turn rope round a pin (Naut.)
44 Mountain crest
45 Donkeys
47 Husband and wife
48 Granny, for one
49 Miss Horne
51 Sailor
53 Smash
54 Recorder (rare)
57 Detecting device
59 Jewish home festival
62 One of the "Little Women"
64 Lily, in France
67 Melville hero
69 Scour
70 Motion picture award

71 Dish of a balance
72 Recorded
74 Jacob's brother
75 Scrimp
76 Harasser
77 City in Iowa
79 Eagle's home
80 Kind of Persian rug
81 Revoke a legacy
83 Captain's record
86 Mark Twain hero
88 Scottish Gaelic
90 A relative
91 Military projectile
93 Most trite
95 Pampers
98 Dorothy Hamill
100 African fly
102 Alan Ladd film
103 Warm compress
105 Synthetic fiber
106 English author
107 Man's name
108 Small particle
109 Isles off Eire
111 Serpent sound
114 Galatea loved him
115 French composer
116 Winter vehicle
119 I love (L.)

PUZZLE 183

ACROSS
1 California pro bowler
6 Pome fruits
11 A step
16 Salty
17 Chemical element
18 Florida pro bowler
20 Oregon pro bowler
21 Mountain crest
22 Wandering
24 A wing
25 Reach
27 City in Cuba
29 Japanese statesman
30 European river
32 Morays
33 Small violins
34 Girl's name
35 Summits
37 Roman 604
39 Bowling target
40 A caster
41 Last six lines of a sonnet
43 Kind of dye
45 Scoffs
46 Air: comb. form
48 "— My Way"
49 Isles off Ireland
50 New York pro bowler
54 Permit
55 One to whom money is due

59 Kitchen need
60 Persian fairies
62 Mark in bowling
64 Food fish
65 Even score
66 Hard to crack
67 Soul, in France
68 Seize roughly
69 Being
71 Missouri pro bowler
73 Eva's friend
75 The cetacea
76 A class of aquatic animals
78 Sense organ
80 Repeats
82 Bills (abbr.)
83 Greek island
85 Uttered
86 Kind of brass
89 Michigan pro bowler
91 Bowler's goal
95 Handle with skill
96 Shinto temples
97 Young salmon
99 Genus of mosquitoes
100 Greek letter
101 To burn
102 Row
104 Poses for a portrait
105 An acid (abbr.)
106 African antelopes

108 Part of the ear
110 Samoan warrior
111 A gazelle
113 Useful
115 Washington pro bowler
117 To delegate
118 Taste
119 American novelist
120 More unusual
121 Corners
122 Musical themes

DOWN
1 Makes obeisance
2 Corrida cheer
3 Kind of cotton
4 Growing out
5 Leased
6 Lauding
7 Deserve
8 American humorist
9 New Jersey pro bowler
10 Moving furtively
11 Old Anglo-Saxon coins
12 Mountain lakes
13 Anglo-Irish expletive
14 Greenland Eskimo
15 A suite
16 Comfort
19 Wisconsin pro bowler

20 Spanish houses
23 Layers of paint
26 Auk genus
28 Wisteria, for one
31 Keep
34 Peaceful
36 Ooze
38 Stringed instruments
39 Sold in pubs
40 Dressed
42 Golfer's nemesis
44 Norwegian statesman
45 Liberate
47 Needed in poker
49 Checks
50 Balloter
51 Dispatch boat
52 Cure by smoking (Scot.)
53 Island off Venezuela
55 New Jersey pro bowler
56 Dogma
57 Declaim
58 Worn by judges
61 Native of: a suffix
63 El —; a mountain in Venezuela
70 Phantoms
71 Late Texas pro bowler
72 Erects

73 Walk heavily (var.)
74 Affirmatives
75 Frameworks
77 Pen for sheep
79 Doctor's org.
81 Gam or Moreno
83 Perennial song hit
84 Defames
86 Still to be paid
87 Made unruly scene
88 Chemical compound
89 A Tai Mongoloid
90 Assam silkworm
92 Certan alcohols
93 Chemical compound
94 Attempt
96 Bartender's need
98 A meal
101 The coltsfoot (dial. Eng.)
103 French security
106 Ivory (Lat.)
107 Asterisk
108 Wild plum
109 Small stalk
112 Mineral spring
114 Common contraction
116 Babylonian god (var.)

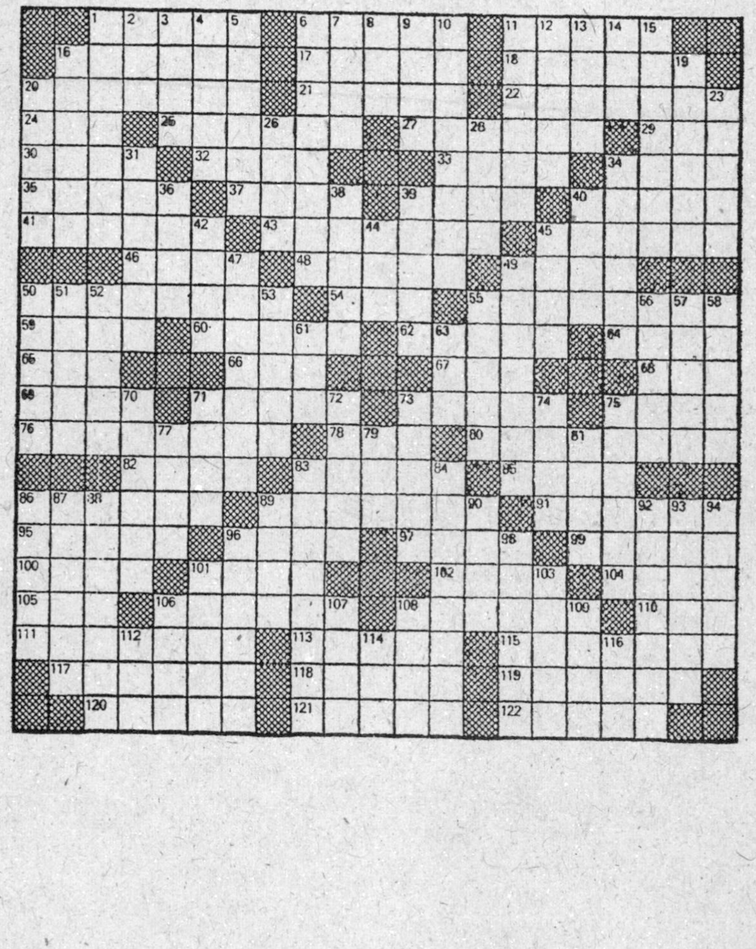
1 2 3 4 5 6 7 8 9 10 11 12 13 14 15
16 17 18 19
20 21 22 23
24 25 26 27 28 29
30 31 32 33 34
35 36 37 38 39 40
41 42 43 44 45
46 47 48 49
50 51 52 53 54 55 56 57 58
59 60 61 62 63 64
65 66 67 68
69 70 71 72 73 74 75
76 77 78 79 80 81
82 83 84 85
86 87 88 89 90 91 92 93 94
95 96 97 98 99
100 101 102 103 104
105 106 107 108 109 110
111 112 113 114 115 116
117 118 119
120 121 122

PUZZLE 184

ACROSS

1 Talon
5 Poe's bird
10 Harbinger of spring
15 Surpasses
19 Blood: comb. form
20 City in New York
21 Sultan's decree
22 Wings
23 One's own: comb. form
24 Adjective suffix
25 Evergreen tree
26 Dark region on Mars
27 Songbird
29 Disease of sheep
31 Relative of 10 Across
33 TV star
34 Young sheep
36 Traduce
37 Destitute
40 Charming
42 Ascends
46 Blore and Portman
47 The urial
48 Oily cyclic ketone
50 Consumed
51 Songbird
52 Corrupt
54 Male duck
56 St. Philip —
57 Native of: a suffix
58 Sudden sharp pains
60 Pitchers
62 River island
63 Calming
65 Raises
67 Walks easily
69 Hop kiln
70 They express grief
71 Gunther's "Inside — "
72 Blue titmouse (Local Eng.)
75 Delibes opera
76 Wastes
80 Labor org.
81 European finch
83 Kind of triangle
85 Lease
86 Russian towns
88 Style of type
90 Onward
91 Serf, once
92 Sheeplike
94 Enclosures for parakeets
96 Valiant Samoan warrior
97 Eastern Christian
98 Repair a shoe
100 Advanced study group
102 Bay windows
103 Lasted under use
105 Appraiser
106 Macaws
107 European bullfinches
111 Detective (slang)
112 Passerine birds
116 Hillside dugout
117 Vegetable caterpillar
119 Complete
121 Dies —
122 Sandarac tree
123 Fearful
124 Worship
125 Hills of Assam
126 Actor: Stephen —
127 Anoint (archaic)
128 Works as a cowboy
129 Secluded valley

DOWN

1 Sartorially smart
2 Mother of Castor and Pollux
3 Mohammedan noble
4 Game bird
5 Destroyed
6 Essence of roses
7 Stringed instrument
8 Old French coin
9 Pre-Incan Indian
10 Java sparrow
11 Money of account
12 Kind of pigeon
13 Baal, and others
14 A celestial structure
15 Welsh
16 Turkish regiment
17 Young salmon
18 Food for birds
28 Stitchbirds
30 All: comb. form
32 River
34 Oriental weight
35 Sleep disturbers
37 Greek island
38 One of the Muses
39 Oscine bird
40 Interjection imitative of sound
41 Bites with effort
43 Purloin
44 Uncanny
45 Fits of pique
47 Charteris hero
49 Supplement
52 A tornado
53 Sandpiper
55 Expunging
58 Massenet opera
59 Lines of junction
61 Strike
64 Toddler
66 Betel palm
68 Dracula's alter ego?
70 Oscine bird
71 Sphere of action
72 Island of the Malay Archipelago
73 Popeye's sweetie
74 — Stella; Star of the sea
75 Nutritious beans
76 Ground surface
77 Famous cow
78 Of the kidneys
79 Marks to let stand
82 Fabulous bird
84 Place of sacrifice
87 The ivory gull
89 A roundworm
91 Isolating
93 Word in Mark 15:34
95 Location
97 Mountain range
99 Printing errors
101 Drink of the gods
102 Papal veils
104 — Drood; a Dickens character
106 Cognizant
107 East Indian coarse sugar
108 River in Spain
109 Strong low cart
110 Sown (Her.)
112 Road sign
113 Evangelist Roberts
114 Carry on, as war
115 — O'Casey
118 Sesame
120 Half brother of William I

PUZZLE 185

ACROSS

1 Semite
5 Before, tc a sailor
10 Empty
15 River to the Danube
19 A palm wine
20 A thermoplastic
21 Eagle's home
22 Baseball team
23 Kind of knot
25 Insecure fastening
27 Anglo-Saxon letter
28 Soothe
29 Meadow
31 Yucatan Indian
32 A fuel
33 Giant grass
35 Flowerless plants
37 Yuccalike plant
39 Vicar's assistant
41 Dwells
43 Sea nymph
46 The tarsus
47 Danish weights
48 Biblical name
50 A name of Indra
51 Cord or wire
52 Mexican coin
53 Culture medium
55 Obstacle

56 Card game
57 Franciscans
59 Fur pieces
61 Indian
62 Star in Scorpio
64 Sharp
66 To level
68 Roman 504
69 Corrida cheer
70 Crude metal
71 Student
75 Plays boisterously
77 Scintillate
81 Size of coal
82 Young lion
84 Drunken carousals
86 Domestic pigeon
87 House wings
89 Burden
90 Bellow
91 Ibsen heroine
92 Pixielike
94 Very, in – France
96 Pickler's need
97 Word with jury or larceny
98 Physician
100 Exhaust
102 A Zoroastrian
103 Street show
105 Protective ditches
106 French painter
107 I love (L.)

109 Coarse hominy
111 Never (Ger.)
112 Girl's name
113 Noun suffix
116 Kind of knot
119 Kind of knot
122 River in Italy
123 Uncanny
124 Large cat
125 Roman 1102
126 Overmatch
127 Arrange in folds
128 Marks to let stand
129 Light: comb. form

DOWN

1 French cleric
2 Marsh grass
3 Fisherman's bend
4 American editor
5 Wily
6 Aesop's forte
7 Russian city
8 Sought office
9 Continuous
10 A people of Uganda
11 Irish sea god
12 Biblical land
13 Little girls, in Spain
14 Early actress: Doris –
15 India, for one
16 Kind of knot

17 Wild ox
18 Soaks flax
24 Gladden
26 English novelist
30 Son of God
34 Story
35 Man's hat
36 Staid
38 Danish money
39 Showy lily
40 Junction
41 Painter Bonheur
42 Edible starch
44 Very angry
45 Philistine deity
47 Hawaiian garlands
49 Division of a football game
52 Triumph
54 Let down again
57 Fluted edging
58 To dart
59 Degrees
60 Garments for Indira
63 Commotion
65 City on the Danube
67 Denary
71 Celerity
72 Musical instrument
73 Certain knots
74 Origin
75 Ransom
76 Nautical spars

77 River duck
78 Used in embroidery
79 Political cartoonist
80 Growing out
83 Fragrant ointment
85 Part
88 Wife of Rama-chandra
91 Pianist Peter
93 Scandinavians
95 Poetic foot
96 Discovers
97 Bombay measure
99 Raised upright
101 Medieval tale
102 Knotty problems
104 Live coal
106 Perfume ingredient
107 Melville's captain
108 Dark area on the moon
110 Constan-tinople's foreign quarter
112 Theater section
114 Shadow: comb. form
115 Not that
117 Drunkard
118 Pinch
120 Illumined
121 Mischievous child

PUZZLE 186

ACROSS

1 Capital of Latvia
5 Yawning abyss
10 Windy month
15 Go to the store
19 Man's name
20 Capital of North Vietnam
21 Worship
22 Large volume
23 Indian grindstone
24 Dilate
25 Language of a people
26 Algerian seaport
27 A windy city
29 Murdered
30 French composer
31 Aside
32 U.S. playwright
34 Old Dutch measure
36 Entrap
38 Brigade commander (abbr.)
41 Pronoun
42 Of the moon
44 Understand
45 Neighbor of Can.
48 — Hayward, late Broadway producer
50 Brief swim suits
52 Indian war trophies
54 Astound
55 Rescues
56 Common value
58 Wide awake
59 Famous fiddler
60 Uncanny
61 American novelist
63 Arabian chieftain
64 A windy city
66 Skin tumor
67 A windy city
69 Falls behind
70 Proscribe
71 Chinese pagodas
72 A windy city
76 Droop
77 A windy city
82 Notion
83 Anesthetic
85 To squander
86 Part
87 Walk crabwise
89 Sense organ
90 Pale tinges
91 Late singer Bobby —
92 Written in verse
94 An ancient people
96 A windy city
97 Relatives of aves.
98 Underworld god
100 Coagulates
101 Excavate
102 Greek letter
103 Lariat
105 Watch pocket
106 Weathercocks
108 — Sadat
111 Arabic letter
113 Shore bird
115 Young cod
119 Secluded corner
120 Biblical name
121 French school
123 Incarnation of Vishnu
124 Painful
125 Gold or silver
126 Edgar — Poe
127 Avouch
128 Picnic pests
129 January, in Barcelona
130 Marrow (Scot.)
131 Saucy

DOWN

1 San —, Italy
2 Moslem leader
3 Actress Lollobrigida
4 Hawaiian greeting
5 Chapters (abbr.)
6 Towing rope
7 Anoint (archaic)
8 Flatfish
9 A windy city
10 Post office worker
11 Egyptian skink
12 Muddies
13 Sings softly
14 Surround
15 Ore excavation
16 Lively dance
17 Sharif or Bradley
18 Confined
28 Perennial song favorite
31 Betal palm
33 Plant shoot
35 Cuckoos
37 Roman bronze
38 Mont —
39 Paired
40 Irish county
42 Black and blue
43 Mature
45 Body of Moslem scholars
46 Small twig
47 Houston player
49 Sea of —
50 Rural buildings
51 Speak
53 Fish sauce
55 Channel to the sea
57 Remodels
60 Gladden
61 Cognizance
62 Disgrace
65 Wallach or Whitney
66 Oscillate
68 Equal: comb. form
70 Legal profession
71 Examines
72 Small bunches
73 Mental deficient
74 Yields
75 Military command
76 Pinnacle of glacier ice
77 Hamlet and Borge
78 Gershwin and Levin
79 North wind, in Spain
80 English novelist
81 Dried cassia leaflets
84 Possesses
85 Certain protective shelter
88 Sea duck
90 Novice
91 Venetian magistrates
93 Govt. org.
95 A windy city
96 Storage compartment
99 Flower part
101 A windy city
103 Roues
104 Winged
106 French musical instrument
107 A shred
108 Handle
109 Midday
110 Herb
112 Munich's river
114 Asiatic tree
116 Rant
117 Hebrew measure
118 Pub missile
120 French spirit
122 Noun suffix

PUZZLE 187

ACROSS

1 Sun-dried brick
6 To skin
10 A rebuff
14 Philippine island
19 French politician
20 Grass genus
21 Verdi opera
22 Wear away
23 Brains (colloq.)
25 Old men
27 River islands
28 Pulsates
30 Wild ox
31 Brewer's need
32 Compass reading
33 Merriment
34 A fuel
36 Spicy stew
38 An affirmative
39 Gray with age
40 Odysseus's dog
42 Dolomites
44 Respects
47 Figwort genus
49 Long, wearying attacks
53 Sheeplike
54 Carbuncle (Fr.)
55 Havens for travelers
57 Plowed land
58 Cereal food
59 Biblical name
60 Children's nurses
62 Genus of the bowfin
63 Summer drink
64 Light carriage
65 Tetrahedrite
67 Cooking flavoring
68 Not any
69 The cottontail
75 Unite firmly
78 Swiss river
81 Goals
82 Indigent
83 Mountain crest
84 To eye
85 Struck
87 Prophet
88 Russian hemp
89 Group of three
90 Mother or father
92 Exerted a reciprocal influence
94 Drawing rooms
96 Author of "Utopia"
97 Falls in crystals
98 Twining stem
99 Legal profession
102 Warble
104 High, craggy hill
105 Submerged
106 Deface
109 Biblical name
111 Case for small articles
113 Approach quietly
115 Desert in Asia
116 Franciscans
119 Butternut
121 Sea duck
122 Riding whip
123 Walk or tramp
124 Card wool
125 Lariat
126 Author Ferber
127 Used a golf peg
128 Mountain chain

DOWN

1 Seaweeds
2 Late singer: Bobby —
3 Egg-shaped
4 Arms of the sea
5 Stately tree
6 Priest's title
7 Measure of capacity
8 Mars: comb. form
9 Hand with no card higher than a 9
10 Droop
11 Spend it in Venice
12 "A Bell for — "
13 Kind of graft
14 Bishopric
15 Ancient country
16 Voracious eel
17 Make confused
18 Takes five
24 Burden-bearer
26 Formal dances
29 Portent
33 Author Vidal
35 Mislaying
37 Samoan seaport
39 Sharpen
40 Medicinal plants
41 Detecting device
43 Mexican blanket
44 Lively dance
45 Roman poet
46 French resort
47 In the style of
48 " — Karenina"
50 Umbrella
51 Comedienne Adams
52 European river
54 Island of Indonesia
56 Short music drama
58 Heathen
61 Teacake
64 Elevator cage
66 Canadian prov.
67 Method
69 Pant
70 Philippine breadfruit
71 God of love
72 Tavern order
73 Notions (Fr.)
74 Despot
75 English inventor
76 Indians
77 Repair
78 Exchange premium
79 Alda or King
80 Cincinnati players
84 Voided escutcheon
86 Adam's grandson
89 Cistern
91 City on the Moselle
93 Rail bird
94 Tendon
96 Lure
98 Kept afloat
99 Companion of lox
100 Entrance courts
101 Peruses
103 Protect
105 Prospector's need
106 A unit
107 Mistreat
108 Ceremonies
110 Gypsy gentlemen
112 Chemical element
114 — - dieu
115 Secluded valley
117 To and —
118 Resort
120 One — time

PUZZLE 188

ACROSS

1 Whip
5 Motive
10 Measure of length
15 Salvia
19 Soothe
20 Bowling lane
21 Declaim
22 Medicinal plant
23 Celebes ox
24 For the — ; temporarily
25 Angers
26 Baal, for one
27 Corsage flower
29 Today's frontier
31 Claws
33 Gershwin and Levin
34 The march king
35 Source of poi
36 Wands for conductors
39 Asparagus, et al.
40 Fragrant flower
44 Soap plant
45 Timber trees
46 Kind of lily
47 Liquid measures (abbr.)
48 Queen of the gods, in Egypt
49 Columbus sailed from here
50 Bast fiber
51 Jacket or collar
52 Wrath
53 Drunkard
54 Dried orchid tubers
55 Golfer's Waterloo
56 Delphinium
58 Coconut and betel
59 Vertical pipes
60 California valley
61 Talisman, et al.
62 British gun
63 Art of hunting
66 European capital
67 The common anemone
71 Zodiac sign
72 The hills of Rome
73 Charity festivals
74 Consumed
75 Author of "Atlas Shrugged"
76 Fields
77 Italian poet
78 Quote
79 WWII area
80 Song for Ida Lupino
81 Confronts
82 Swiss canton
83 Yews and pines
85 To have recourse
86 Buffoons
87 Withered
88 Netherlands city
89 Slender, strong cord
90 Sucking fish
93 — voce
94 Source of digitalis
98 Dutch cheese
99 Extinct Haitian Indian
101 To drench
103 Animal's bed
104 Dreadful
105 Austrian botanist
106 Bury
107 Natives: a suffix
108 Play the lead
109 French painter
110 Unstratified loam deposit
111 The caama

DOWN

1 The iris
2 Moon-goddess
3 Swan genus
4 Plants of the iris family
5 Showy flowers
6 Man's name
7 Forearm bone
8 Wine quality
9 Unpleasant sights
10 Swamp
11 Heather
12 "Canterbury" segment
13 Nice season
14 Give horse a new home
15 Sinbad, for one
16 Actor — Ray
17 Hired thug
18 Morays
28 Sea bird
30 Plays on words
32 Region
34 Spanish gentleman
35 Cultivated bulb
36 Mountain mint
37 Genus of ground beetles
38 Stone roller; a fish
39 Office worker
40 Domesticates
41 Ocular
42 Gillyflower
43 Serfs
45 New Guinea
46 Soothes
49 Showy flower
50 Chest sounds
51 Antelope
53 Peter and Ivan
54 The black buck
55 Frets
57 Green foxtail
58 Minute openings
59 To hoard
61 Poe's bird
62 Fits of pique
63 Seaweed
64 One of the Muses
65 Curtain fabric
66 Persian fairies
67 More rational
68 Elevate
69 Aquatic mammal
70 Pares
72 Frighten
73 Plane surface of a diamond
76 Garden flower
77 Spring flower
78 Ornamental flowering shrub
80 Southwest wind
81 Sensed
82 Mr. Crosby
84 Chemical compound
85 Lab vessel
86 Sociable people
88 One receiving the gift
89 Comes in second
90 Cincinnati team
91 Wield a blue pencil
92 Naomi's chosen name
93 Portent
94 Eskimo curlew
95 Food for horses
96 Competes
97 Scottish Gaelic
100 Miscellany
102 An ass: comb. form

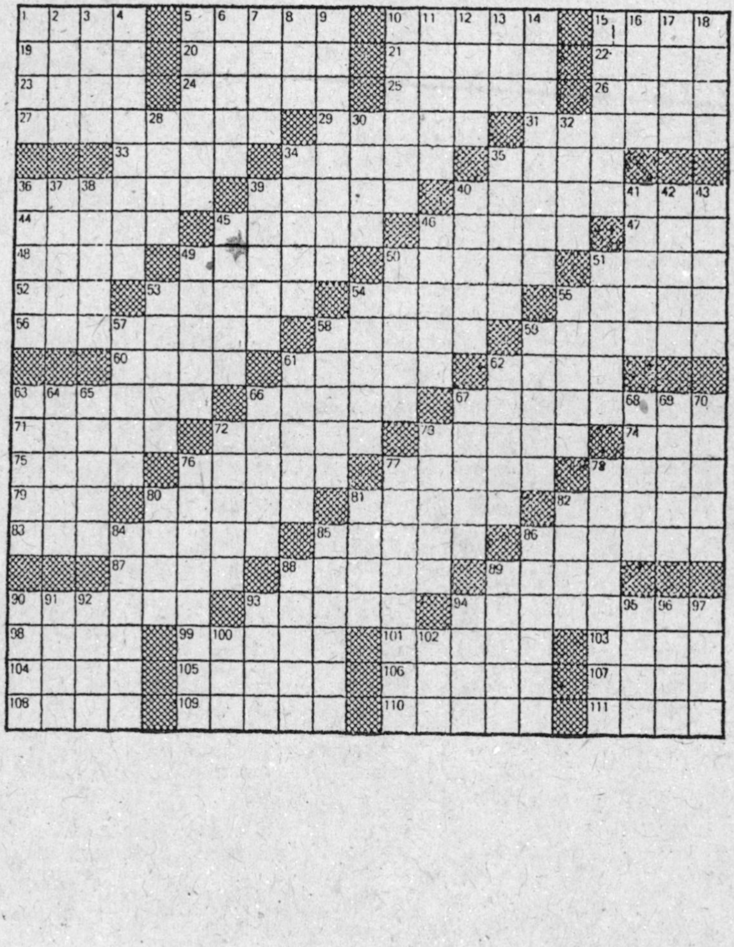

PUZZLE 189

ACROSS

1 Rascal
6 Mexican dish
10 Clan strife
14 Mud volcano
19 Article of virtu
20 Arabian country
21 Biblical word of reproach
22 City on the Moselle
23 Record of a single year
24 Field event
26 One of the Beatles
27 Female ruff
28 Arabian chieftain
30 Oriental coin
31 Subtle emanation
33 A goad
34 Controversial
36 Musical composition
38 Flower-decked spring sight
40 Legal profession
41 Immature frog
43 Torme or Ferrer
44 Nobleman
47 Assesses
48 Overhead railways
50 Put off
54 Ireland
55 Strode back and forth
56 Cure hams
58 Dog of tropical America
59 Small child
60 Strange
61 Tom's penchant
63 Skill
64 Disputation
66 English divine and poet
67 Prominence near the ear (Anat.)
69 Inventor Howe
70 Use block letters
71 Brittle
72 Feel contrition
74 Also called urao
75 Tall, thin boy
78 Artificial language
79 Most weird
81 Depends
82 Malay gibbon
83 Shaded walk
85 Slight depressions
86 Dean Martin TV specialty
87 Queen or First Lady
88 Daub
90 Mature
91 Intervening, in law
92 Imitation gems
93 Cognizance
95 Lures
97 American editor
98 A skunk
102 Moslem coin
103 Long-handled weapon

107 Money of account
108 Ancient Greek coin
110 Labium
111 Strong impulse
112 Majors or Marvin
113 Ocean vessel
115 Carved Indian pillar
118 Observed
120 Evening (Ger.)
121 Verify (L.)
122 Greek underground
123 Not those
124 Ascends
125 Leases
126 Low haunts
127 Large artery

DOWN

1 Steep declivity
2 Wedge-shaped: comb. form
3 Synthetic fiber
4 Actress Farrow
5 Kind of surveyor
6 Subject matter
7 Love god
8 Presidential nickname
9 Unilateral
10 Former Spanish ruler
11 Water, in Paris
12 West Coast univ.
13 A fact
14 Wandered
15 Greek nickname
16 Language
17 George or Vivienne
18 Wear away
25 Rockefeller and Mondale (colloq.)
29 Russian community
32 Ewe's mate
35 Black
36 Eucharistic plate
37 Constituent part
39 An excuse
41 Musical direction
42 Escape the wedding cost
44 Greek letter
45 Sandarac tree
46 Highest roof timber
47 Sheds copiously
49 Enjoy the slopes
51 Seen at forts
52 Beige
53 Decomposes
55 Folded
56 Cassia leaves
57 Applicant for admission
60 Ammonia compound
61 To aim
62 Smiles broadly
65 Rubber tree
66 Waste matter
68 Viper
70 Make believe
71 Come to an end
72 Edges
73 Dutch cheese
74 Slight trace
75 Legumes
76 Endure
77 Scottish Gaelic
80 The turmeric
81 Also-ran
84 George or Louise
86 Repaired a tire
87 Prepare
89 Puts on tape
91 Half note
92 Italian porridge
94 Snatch away (slang)
96 Lodge doorkeepers
97 Morass
98 Word with bear or lights
99 African antelope
100 Bowling alleys
101 Complete
103 Newspapers, collectively
104 Change
105 Cure by smoking (Scot.)
106 Jason was her lover
109 Ardent affection
111 — Bator
114 Compass reading
116 Asian festival
117 Corrida cheer
119 Exclamation

PUZZLE 190

ACROSS
1 Petty quarrel
5 To scrimp (colloq.)
10 Might be made of birchbark
15 French town
19 Wild buffalo of India
20 Poet of the Lake school
21 Greek marketplace
22 Very, in France
23 A fuel
24 Declaim
25 More unusual
26 Island of the Hebrides
27 Found in a regatta
29 Weight, in India
31 Naval vessel
33 Irish clan
34 Smoked meat
36 Unable to hear
37 Trains gun on target
40 Harbor boat
42 Smart (colloq.)
46 Hillside dugouts
47 Audio's companion
48 Animal doc
50 Marsh bird
51 Vault
52 Leaping amphibians
53 Ananias, et al.
55 Greek portico
56 Son of Gad
57 He wrote "Winnie-the-Pooh"
58 Venetian taxi
60 Wander
61 Found the solution
63 Palm cockatoo
65 Statisticians
67 French islands
69 Light rowboat
71 Blemish
72 Man's name, in Italy
76 Genus of geese
78 Localities
82 Wallach or Whitney
83 Communicates, in a way
85 Affray
87 Skill
88 People (Fr.)
90 Michelangelo masterpiece
91 Virulent
92 Conifer, in Spain
93 Negative ion
95 The "diamond" girl
96 Pill for a horse
97 Florentine iris
98 Chinese boat
100 Character in "Aida"
102 Wading birds
103 Elliptical
105 Chapters of the Koran
106 Scotch rivulet
107 Ancient galleys
111 Operated
112 Ancient leather-covered boats
116 Time of day: comb. form
117 Senseless
119 — Bow, the "It" girl
121 Nobleman
122 Minor prophet
123 City in Michigan
124 Animal fat
125 Capital of Latvia
126 Polynesian forest god
127 Insect pests
128 Accumulate
129 Weather word

DOWN
1 Indians
2 Malayan canoe
3 Philippine termite
4 Participant in "Operation Sail"
5 Fore-and-aft-rigged vessels
6 Gem weight (var.)
7 Silk fabric of Sumatra
8 Satisfied
9 Portends
10 Vegetable
11 Turkish officer
12 Standard
13 Mountain nymph
14 Deserved
15 Becomes rigid
16 Scottish catamaran
17 Russian river
18 Eskers
28 Wagers
30 She loved Narcissus
32 Paddles
34 Auction participants
35 American composer
37 Auctions
38 Iberian: comb. form
39 Chalice
40 Climbing plant
41 Peruses
43 Locations
44 Polo, for one
45 Time periods
47 Volunteer (abbr.)
49 Jogs
52 A tidal wave
53 Lounges idly
54 Cuffed
57 Dissolves
58 Smiles broadly
59 Gruel of maize meal
62 Compete
64 Hawaiian fruit
66 Greenland Eskimo
68 A seal
70 Women
72 French painter
73 Turgenev heroine
74 Half note, in music
75 Dream: comb. form
77 Form of riddle
79 Mound of stones
80 One of the Fords
81 Facing glacier direction
84 Burden-bearer
86 French lily
89 Full of sleep
91 Certain novels
92 Caperers
94 Church part
96 Silent star: Theda —
97 Odd (Scotch)
99 Nominating
101 Compulsion
102 Arrow poison
104 Russian leader
106 Tree pest
107 The one there
108 City in Italia
109 Chemical element
110 Spanish dining hall
112 Roman patriot
113 Reclined
114 Therefore
115 Cabbage salad
118 Word with profit
120 Military vessel

PUZZLE 191

ACROSS

1 Venomous snake
6 Venomous snake
11 Venomous snake
16 Hold in custody
17 Genus of grasses
18 Cried hollowly
20 — Islands; West Pacific Ocean
21 Ceremonies
22 Like snakes
24 Brazilian birds
25 French schools
27 Apple or pear
29 Open receptacle
30 Insect egg
31 Opens (poetic)
32 Subtle emanation
33 White House initials
34 Bishoprics
36 Fit of pique
37 Authenticate officially
39 Pub order
40 Netherlands city
42 Up to the time of
43 Warning signals
45 Queen of heaven
46 The sun personified
47 Heard at the Met
48 Black snakes
51 A faux pas
52 Fabulous serpent
56 Early president
57 Bridges (Fr.)
58 Caravansary
59 Regret
60 Twining stem
61 Asian country
62 Song of joy
63 Tree snake
64 Crushing snake
65 Publicized
66 Actress Marta —
67 Civetlike animal
68 Hawaii resident
70 Venomous snake
71 Vacillates
72 Recollection
73 Satisfies
74 Measure of length
75 African antelope
78 Customs
79 Assembles
83 Periods of time
84 Locales
86 Legendary Swiss archer
87 Scat!
88 Common suffix
89 Grampuses
90 Biblical name
91 A continent (abbr.)
92 London district
94 Nick Charles' pet dog
95 Snaky-haired Gorgon
97 Ready (Fr.)
98 Cancer and Capricorn
100 Endure
102 Serpentine
104 Scythe handle
105 Angry
106 Captivate
107 Wild plums
108 Saltpeter
109 French senate

DOWN

1 Waxy ointments
2 American inventor
3 Rural sound
4 Russian hemp
5 Large crushing snake
6 Scoundrel
7 Japanese and Swedish
8 Favorites
9 Chemical suffix
10 Russian monk
11 South American serpents
12 An opiate
13 Palm fiber
14 Discharge
15 Rearrange
16 Town in Connecticut
19 A crown
20 Clergyman's home
23 Stainers
26 English painter
28 Soviet city
32 Essence of roses
35 To plot
36 Weights of India
37 Feeds the kitty
38 Kind of bone
39 Pagan god
41 Word on towels
42 Mountains in Utah
44 Roman 53
46 Modified in color
47 Baseball great
48 Jewish teacher
49 Farewell, in Madrid
50 Panama or Suez
51 Tree pest
52 Soft cap
53 Oily cyclic ketone
54 More certain
55 English poet
57 Studied
58 Garments for Indira
61 Carry off for ransom
62 Covers with protective layer
63 Morning receptions
65 Dye indigo
66 Kilmer subject
67 Sore caused by chafing
69 Chalices
70 Keresan Indian
71 Force of mind
73 Pit viper
74 Treacle
75 That is (L.)
76 Mansions (obs.)
77 Large, non-venomous snakes
78 An emporium
79 Philippine island
80 Type of cigar
81 French towboat
82 Classifies
85 Amounts of decrease
86 Hay spreader
90 French security
93 Gem stone
94 Dull pain
95 Goddess of justice
96 Senior (Fr.)
97 The cougar
99 Japanese statesman
101 Three: a prefix
103 Girl's nickname

PUZZLE 192

ACROSS

1 Nourish
5 Corded fabrics
9 Chinese pagodas
13 The rainbow
17 Churchman-author
18 Case for small articles
19 God of fire
20 Wanderer
22 A watchful guardian
23 Vessels for apothecaries
25 Aesop's forte
26 Crane fly
28 European water hen
30 English rural festival
31 — Descartes
32 Unused
34 Origin
35 Poet's word
36 Site of the Leaning Tower
37 Long blouse
39 River to the North Sea
41 University governor
44 " — and Old Lace"
46 Encomiums
50 Anthropoid ape
51 Earth: comb. form
52 Greek letters
54 Gaze steadily
55 Gentle
56 To cringe
59 Early canal
61 Genus of auks
62 Red dye
63 Chinese city
65 Frightens suddenly
67 — Allen
69 The white goose (Hindu myth.)
71 Kilmer poem
72 Concurring
75 Strong inclination
77 Jones or Edison
80 Quarter, for one
81 Muck
83 Hardens
84 Wander
85 Contemptible one
87 Iranian Turk
89 Sesame
90 French painter
91 Polish general
93 Street or liquor
96 Stop watches
97 Onion
99 Madame de —, French writer
100 Queen or First Lady
101 Simpleton
104 Office note
106 Exclamation of disgust
107 Gilead's descendant
108 Assistance
111 Word peculiar to French
114 An absurd medley
117 Inventor Howe
118 Roam about for pleasure
120 Bike's relative
121 Evade by craft
122 Migratory worker
123 Biblical king
124 Burdens
125 Role for Robert Stack
126 Rescue
127 Prescribed amount of medicine
128 Worked in the garden

DOWN

1 Wild
2 Predatory bird
3 Hebrew month
4 Craving
5 Victoria —
6 Public storehouse
7 Soft, succulent part
8 Minor woodland deity
9 Faucet
10 Excited
11 Brazilian tapirs
12 French painter
13 Kaffirs
14 Kind of horse
15 To saturate
16 French hall
17 Philippine rice
21 "The — Hunter"
24 Goddess of peace
27 Cozy place
29 — majesty
33 Port or chianti
36 Await settlement
37 Conduit for water
38 Quote
40 Turn
41 City in Italia
42 Assam silkworm
43 Fitted with corridorlike passages
44 An age of the world
45 Reo and Edsel
47 Painful bodily obstruction
48 Author Gardner
49 Bishoprics
51 American editor
53 Don't slump in your chair!
56 — Weizmann, first president of Israel
57 Split, as the skin
58 Biblical name
60 Merits
63 Haggard novel
64 Common contraction
66 Soak flax
68 Animal of Madagascar
70 Cellulose acetate
72 Recorded proceedings
73 A loose robe
74 Seize roughly
76 French exclamation
78 Above
79 Baseball team
82 God of love
84 Gypsy boys
86 Antecedent happenings
88 Ballerina's skirt
90 Pair unsuitably
92 Special (abbr.)
94 East Indian cereal grass
95 Minded one's manners
96 Sport group
98 Friends, in Spain
100 Jocular
101 Full of years
102 Drawing room
103 Slip
105 Japanese city
107 Forearm bones
108 Ablaze
109 Annoyed
110 Stains
112 Loiters
113 Roman 1,054
115 French composer
116 Pure form of trona
119 Famous general

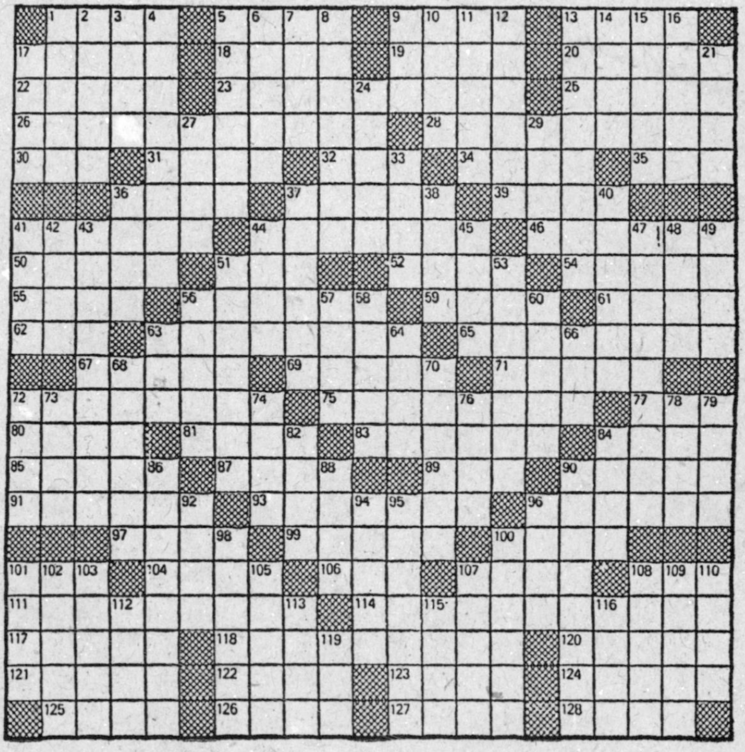

ACROSS

1 Pinnacle of glacier ice
6 Church part
10 Biblical place
14 Willow
19 Palm cockatoo
20 Indian
21 Branches
22 Actress Duncan
23 Hindu guitar
24 Eternities
25 Fish sauce
26 French physicist and chemist
27 Down at heel
28 Philippinne tree
29 Moved furtively
30 Zodiac sign
31 Religious doubter
34 Tallow: comb. form
36 German article
39 Dwarf
40 King, in France
42 Dye indigo
43 Consumed
46 To wall
48 Insomniac writer
50 They go with colds
52 Cantaloupes
53 Actor Robert —
55 Conserves of grapes
56 Ward off
57 Enjoy a repast
58 Pianist Peter
60 Mountain crest
61 Withered
62 Farm buildings
63 Capital of South Vietnam
65 Chemist's degree
66 Country in Asia
68 TV's Somers
70 Possessed
73 Manservants
76 "Forever —"
78 Vestments
82 Ascend
84 Mark on a galley
85 Man's name
86 Country in South America
87 Figure of speech
90 Cuddle
91 One placing the call
92 African palm
94 They (Fr. fem.)
95 American general
96 Curve of ship's planking
97 French resort
99 Danish measure
100 Noted couturier
101 Harem room
102 Grassy surfaces
104 Turtle's upper shell
107 Stone pillar
110 Afghanistan nomad (var.)
112 Under the weather
113 Detests
117 Islands in the Pacific
118 Precious alloy of Egypt
119 Queen of the gods (Egypt)
120 Tennyson's Isolde
121 In the midst of
122 Musket ball
123 Collar or jacket
124 Lawful
125 Horse's comment
126 Grafted (Her.)
127 Strong taste
128 Spanish-American plain

DOWN

1 Back talk
2 Pennsylvania lake port
3 Appraise
4 Plowed land
5 Insomniac actor
6 Chemical solvent
7 Insomniac author
8 French senate
9 Letters
10 Inland sea
11 Anklebone
12 Catkins
13 Insomniac author
14 Insomniac entertainer
15 Lizard: comb. form
16 Letter phrase
17 Comedienne Adams
18 Gypsy gentlemen
29 Deride
32 Litchi, and others
33 Sultan's decrees
35 Indigenous Japanese
36 Insomniac author
37 French student
38 Governor
41 Sacred images (var.)
43 Mexican Indian
44 Molars, et al.
45 Ancient chariot
47 Actress Sophia —
48 Game of chance
49 Region
51 Sense organ
53 Very small brooks
54 Technique in basketball
57 Uses the phone
59 Fabled monsters
62 Resort
64 Poetic contraction
67 Insomniac author
69 Western lake resort
70 Hinged metal straps
71 Adherent of Arius
72 Obscurely
74 Ribbon: comb.form
75 Mine adit
76 Actress Lansbury
77 Wire measures
79 Dialect
80 Exude sap
81 Junipero —; Spanish missionary
83 Alastair —
86 Insomniac statesman
88 Assam silkworm
90 German composer
91 Malayan canoe
93 Farmer's concern
96 Insomniac author
98 Insomniac inventor
100 Actress Abby —
102 Jargon
103 Edible fish
105 Lariat
106 Studio adjunct
107 Cross over
108 Domesticate
109 Word in Mark 15:34
111 French girlfriend
114 Roman garment
115 Ardor
116 French town
119 Harden

PUZZLE 194

ACROSS

1 To irritate
6 Girls' college in Missouri
11 Girls' college in Illinois
16 Girls' college in New York
17 Ore deposits
18 Eulogies
20 Those owing money
21 Opinions
22 Changed
24 To blunder
25 Harvested
27 Digs into books
29 Education org.
30 Cuckoos
32 Asterisk
33 Observed
34 Scottish inventor
35 Hawaiian geese
37 Enthusiasm (slang)
39 River to the Danube
40 Limber
41 Writing instrument (var.)
43 Expanded
45 Those receiving gifts
46 Site of Nepal
48 A genus of mosquitoes
49 A bobbin
50 Girls' college in Connecticut
54 Swiss river
55 Girls' college in Ohio
59 Red and Coral
60 Biblical name
62 Gambling game
64 Appraise
65 Woeful
66 Dawn goddess
67 Those in office
68 Dancer's cymbals
69 Fish sauce
71 Inward
73 Wrinkles
75 Young herring (Scot.)
76 Girls' college in North Carolina
78 Primate
80 Girls' college in Wisconsin
82 June bugs
83 Mantle
85 Air:comb. form
86 Means of self defense
89 Legendary hero
91 Shuffle cards
95 Habituate
96 Carnegie or Evans
97 He was (L.)
99 He bore a burden
100 Rubber trees
101 Irrational number
102 Granny, for one
104 Jaffe and Levenson
105 Arabic letter
106 One of the Gilbert Islands
108 Hawaiian trees
110 Region (var. comb. form)
111 Salt of acetic acid
113 Common heath
115 Perfectly
117 Greek avenging spirit
118 Ascertain
119 American choreographer
120 Approaches
121 Having rural paths
122 Animal fat

DOWN

1 Girls' college in Pennsylvania
2 White House initials
3 Hebrew instrument
4 Passage charges
5 Substitute
6 Girls' college in Pennsylvania
7 Vacate
8 Fish
9 Licentious
10 Taxes
11 Girls' college in Pennsylvania
12 Revolutionary hero
13 Decomposes
14 Mature
15 Trifoliolate
16 French painter
19 Boil
20 College officials
23 Tropical fruits
26 Reimbursed
28 Metallic element
31 Words in the Psalms
34 First at the finish line
36 Congo tribe
38 Shine
39 Roman roads
40 Learning
42 Father
44 Nabokov heroine
45 Comic artist Browne (poss.)
47 Concurs
49 Passade (Provencal)
50 Its capital is Shillong
51 English hymnologist
52 Consumer advocate
53 Pledged faith
55 Sudden thrust
56 Proportion
57 Italy comb. form
58 Fished for lampreys
61 Explorer Johnson
63 One of the Aesir
70 Trees of Lebanon
71 Ireland
72 Paving slab
73 English author
74 River to the Elbe
75 Small birds
77 Lavish excess affection
79 Kentucky bluegrass
81 Assam silkworm
83 Girls' college in New Jersey
84 Girls' college in New York
86 Girls' college in New York
87 Medieval dagger
88 The wall rue
89 Amazon estuary
90 Zola novel
92 Girls' college in Florida
93 Haltingly
94 Attempt
96 Compulsion
98 An explosive
101 Sylvan deity
103 Ebb and neap
106 Sumatran squirrel shrew
107 Region
108 Israeli city
109 Stone paving block
112 Even the score
114 Hunter or Fleming
116 English rural festival

PUZZLE 195

ACROSS

1 A blessing
5 Babylonian god of earth
10 Fragrance
15 Formless mass
19 Actor Ray
20 Roman official
21 Yuccalike plant
22 Noise of surf on shore
23 Approach
24 Wraps a flag around a staff
25 Decree
26 Medicinal plant
27 He wrote "Tobacco Road"
29 Faucet
31 He wrote "The Big Sleep"
33 Intimation
34 Party-givers
36 Semite
37 Gaze upon
40 To relate
42 Gushes suddenly
46 In the air
47 Submit
48 First vertebra of the neck
50 Palm cockatoo
51 Soft leather
52 Public vehicles
54 Uncanny
56 River to the North Sea
57 Native of: a suffix
58 Mocks
60 Simpleton
62 Cushion
63 An agnostic
65 Kind of puzzle
67 Shorelines
69 Sword hilt
70 Gold was his problem
71 Morose
72 Clever
75 A place
76 Of service at weddings and funerals
80 Land measure
81 Jewish home festival
83 Kind of glass container
85 Gratuity
86 Quantity of paper
88 Sorrow
90 River in France
91 — rosa; the rose apple
92 Sign up for
94 Prepares potatoes
96 Golf gadget
97 To resign
98 He wrote "The Naked and the Dead"
100 Gives assent
102 Harangue
103 Small glass bottle
105 Spicy stews
106 Cold Swiss wind
107 He wrote "The Catcher in the Rye"
111 A vestment
112 He wrote "The Jungle"
116 Elliptical
117 Puts on weight
119 Siamese coins
121 Spanish painter
122 Kind of tale?
123 Bar, in a way (Law)
124 Growing out
125 Mine entrance
126 Wild plum
127 Legal papers
128 Wooden peg
129 Headland

DOWN

1 Judges' bench
2 Olive genus
3 Land held in fee simple
4 With James Hall, he wrote "Mutiny on the Bounty"
5 Protect
6 Mature person
7 Young woman
8 Entire amount
9 Wise old man
10 Not having a septum
11 Poet McKuen
12 Of the ear
13 Kind of coffee
14 Church tables
15 He wrote "Long After Midnight"
16 Lounge
17 Indian
18 Popular beverage
28 Basketball's Chamberlain
30 Nick Charles' dog
32 Valley in California
34 Chopped
35 Foster father of Dionysus
37 English philosopher
38 Gladden
39 Cavities
40 Postulate
41 Nostril
43 Grates
44 Entertain
45 Chalcedonies
47 Scorched
49 Biblical wilderness
52 Wild buckwheat
53 Silken
55 Send with the letter
58 Features of cockpits
59 Plant genus
61 Song hit of 1931
64 Greek letter
66 Fundamental
68 French friend
70 Its capital is Rabat
71 Stare fiercely
72 Seraglio
73 Sphere of action
74 Plural of beatus
75 Novel by George Sand
76 Cooks in butter
77 Mouthlike opening
78 Shy
79 Freshet
82 June bug
84 Carries
87 He wrote "Moby Dick"
89 Fastens again
91 He wrote "Vinegar Puss"
93 Check
95 Vend
97 Circular plate
99 Tattered
101 Stroked lightly
102 Christmas tree garnish
104 Rental contract
106 Please, in Berlin
107 Drunkards
108 Grandparental
109 French composer
110 Ceremony
112 He wrote "The Young Lions"
113 Assistant
114 The rainbow
115 Decomposes
118 Cain's land
120 Up: comb. form

PUZZLE 196

ACROSS

1 Climbers, often
6 Heroic in scale
10 French-German river basin
14 Parts of suits
19 Tennis star
20 Scarlett's home
21 Behold (L.)
22 Strange
23 Former tennis star
24 Spring flowers
26 Showy flower
27 Eskimo knife
28 Gypsy gentlemen
30 Malay isthmus
31 Famous volcano
33 Wind on a spindle
34 Course of study
36 Former senator from Conn.
38 Domestic employees
40 Space module
41 Sausages
43 Flowering vine
44 Kind of lily
47 — Matisse
48 WWII org.
50 Philippine island
54 Macaws
55 Prices
56 Hostile meeting
58 Spanish dining hall
59 High, craggy hill
60 Works in rattan
61 City in Mass.
63 Hood's gun
64 Bookbinder's term
66 Wearies
67 Showy flower
69 Merits
70 Blundered
71 Medium for "The Shadow"
72 A cloak
74 Thick (obs.)
75 A counterpart
78 Noted boxer
79 The sea pink
81 Declares for score
82 Son of Bela
83 Mohammedan priest
85 Gilly flower
86 Sheds for sheep
87 Disembark
88 Tablelands
90 Pedro's aunt
91 Peels
92 Tricks
93 Pronoun
95 Virginia or trumpet
97 Salt, in Paris
98 Flowering shrubs
102 Beats
103 Garden flower
107 Loose, hanging shred
108 An astringent
110 Flower garland
111 Luzon native
112 Greek nickname
113 Half note
115 Garden flowers
118 Award of honor
120 Mountain crest
121 Icelandic measure
122 Tidy
123 Chemical compound
124 More modern
125 Stout, clumsy shoe
126 School problems
127 Biblical name

DOWN

1 A form of riddle
2 Immature seed
3 The stonecrop
4 Work unit
5 More austere
6 Anesthetic
7 Reimburses
8 Author Levin
9 Hens, at times
10 Legislative body
11 Perform
12 Dull pain
13 Musical pauses
14 Annuls
15 High note
16 From the time of
17 General trend
18 Ginger cookies
25 Persian
29 Sweet potato
32 Pinch
35 Islands, in France
36 Ordered at pubs
37 Fished in a certain way
39 Chinese pagodas
41 River to the North Sea
42 Gaiters
44 London gallery
45 Metallic element
46 Fragrant flowers
47 Sharpens
49 Mountain —
51 Flowering trees
52 Turkish regiment
53 Pro —
55 They protect hairdos
56 Anxieties
57 Risks
60 Reiner and Sandburg
61 More faulty
62 Gold-greedy one
65 Light caress
66 Adobe, for one
68 Nothing
70 Outer layer of a fruit
71 Chest sounds
72 Mutilate
73 Egyptian singing and dancing girl
74 Impassive
75 Nero or Ustinov
76 Sea eagle
77 Covers
80 Siamese coin
81 Customs
84 Post
86 Legends under pictures
87 Girl's name
89 Ocean vessel
91 Biblical name
92 Jerusalem thorns
94 Girl of song
96 Fishing for lampreys
97 Harden
98 Madison Avenue denizen
99 The former Belgian Congo
100 Former U.S. Vice-president
101 Poisonous tree
103 Plagues
104 Lowest point
105 Sultan's decree
106 Troubled
109 A shaded walk
111 Furniture designer
114 Native of: a suffix
116 Grande or Bravo
117 Romanian coin
119 Uncle (dial.)

PUZZLE 197

ACROSS

1 Employ
5 Part of 83 Across
10 They march in 85 Down
15 With 94 Across, fireworks features
19 So be it!
20 One of the Muses
21 Opposed to cathode
22 He wrote "Trinity"
23 Barbecue feature
24 Lodge doorkeeper
25 Silly one
26 Tidy
27 Fireworks display
29 With 31 Across, part of a fireworks display
31 See 29 Across
33 Electrified particles
34 Contends
35 Role for Rosalind Russell
36 Earth, for one
39 Mountain ash tree
40 Natives of Catalonia
44 A means to an end
45 Slant
46 Used to light 56 Across
47 Cut off
48 Indians
49 Strode back and forth
50 Compass point
51 Become bankrupt
52 Revolver
53 Stage direction
54 Affray
55 — Via; principal street of ancient Rome
56 Bright fireworks item
58 Kind of cat
59 A noisy firework
60 Hastens
61 Hamlet and Borge
62 Quote
63 Morning prayers
66 Shelter
67 Talked idly
71 Manacles
72 Functions in trigonometry
73 Chopin's instrument
74 Before
75 Withered
76 Pigeons
77 Heraldic device
78 Pulpy fruit
79 Nahoor sheep
80 Misrepresent
81 Teases or goads
82 The common heath
83 With 90 Across, a feature of July 4
85 The external ear
86 Found in 85 Down
87 Not new
88 Anwar —
89 He wrote "The Wizard of Oz"
90 See 83 Across
93 Kind of seal
94 See 15 Across
98 High tableland
99 Seed integument
101 That is (L.)
103 Jog
104 Haze
105 Inward
106 Eagle's home
107 — Gardner
108 To the sheltered side
109 American diplomatist
110 Saltpeter
111 Condiment

DOWN

1 Door fastening
2 Body of Kaffir warriors
3 Check
4 Interlaces
5 That which is held in the mind
6 Sign of the Ram
7 Summon
8 Season in Nice
9 Grieved
10 Underworld collectors
11 Wild oxen
12 Midday
13 Dental degree
14 Adult male seal (Alaska)
15 Chimney or flue
16 Angered
17 Coin of Iran
18 Italian noble family
28 Garden worker
30 Gem stone
32 Oriental nurse
34 Sheltered inlets
35 Dull finish
36 Stopples
37 Abatement (colloq.)
38 Genus of grasses
39 Return
40 Printer's mark
41 Companion of alas
42 Crotchet (Fr.)
43 Part of chair back
45 Bundles
46 Breakwaters
48 Needed by gondoleers
50 "— on Sunday"
51 Gem face
53 Removes the pelt
54 Rich sources
55 — voce
57 River to the North Sea
58 Caverns
59 Laughing
61 One receiving the gift
62 Stupid
63 — cantata
64 Common contraction
65 "Law of Moses"
66 Relating to a citizen
67 Michelangelo masterpiece
68 Novel by George Sand
69 To belch
70 He forsook Paul
72 Firm
73 Use block letters
76 Hated
77 Native of Montreal
78 Advances
80 Win out over
81 To wait
82 Jewish month
84 Crescent-shaped
85 Feature of July 4
86 Hesitate
88 Lucifer
89 Count, of jazz
90 Austen novel
91 To conceal
92 Being
93 This, in Spain
94 Lahr or Parks
95 Odd (Scot.)
96 Oliver's nickname
97 Printer's mark
100 Chemical suffix
102 Agnus —

PUZZLE 198

ACROSS

1 President from Nebraska
5 President from Massachusetts
10 President from Virginia
15 President from Ohio
19 Flowering shrub
20 Nobleman
21 Female of the ruff
22 Arabian chieftain
23 A scar
24 Valuable violin
25 Up to the time of
26 Philippine Moslem
27 President from Virginia
29 Knave of clubs
31 Drooled
33 Kitchen need
34 European herring
36 Asterisk
37 Becomes taut
40 German violinmaker
42 Redactor
46 "Iliad," and others
47 Michelangelo sculpture
48 Never (Ger.)
50 Babylonian hero
51 Austrian physicist
52 Jokes
53 Sheriff's band
55 Mythological Norse giant
56 German exclamation
57 Rail birds
58 Mom and Dad
60 Before
61 Offensive odor
63 Navigation system
65 Perform for practice
67 Sea birds
69 Nostrils
71 Worn by Indira
72 Bewilders
76 Suburb of Boston
78 Dresses stone with hammer
82 Rio de —
83 Saved by housewives
85 Former name of radon
87 Britain's West Point (abbr.)
88 Refuse of grapes
90 Approaches
91 Dravidian language
92 Pouchlike parts
93 St. — fire
95 Hindu title of address
96 Allots
97 President from Ohio
98 Tarts (Eng. var.)
100 Sacred precinct (Gr. Antiq.)
102 He wrote "A Bell for Adano"
103 Pipe or conduit
105 One independent of others
106 Model
107 President from New York
111 Bird's bill
112 President from Vermont
116 Comedienne Adams
117 Western film
119 Laughing
121 Not any
122 Minus
123 Piebald
124 Not chronic
125 And others (abbr.)
126 Makes lace
127 Drudge
128 Kind of seal
129 Hardens

DOWN

1 U.S. statesman
2 Great Barrier Island
3 Elevate
4 U.S. conductor and composer
5 Humbles
6 Friend of Pythias
7 Isles off Eire
8 Witty saying
9 Small scraps
10 President from Missouri
11 Longing
12 Permits
13 Depravities
14 Recount
15 Rash boldness
16 Love god
17 Ignite
18 Trampled
28 Currier and —
30 Heard at the opera
32 Depart (Lat.)
34 Man's hat
35 General trend
37 Musical themes
38 Excess of solar year
39 Wall recess
40 Agave fiber
41 Stair part
43 More docile
44 Unique persons
45 Portable peep show
47 Through
49 Serfs
52 President from Texas
53 The whole jury
54 Alcohol
57 Eliminate (colloq.)
58 Yugoslavian coins
59 Finch
62 Ship-shaped clock
64 Grates
66 Assistance
68 Male and female
70 Gravel or Bumpers
72 Heavenly body
73 Papal veil
74 Constellation in the Milky Way
75 Commence
77 Buffoons
79 Asa and Thomas
80 Master of ceremonies
81 Impudent (colloq.)
84 Bay window
86 Poet's word
89 Operated by batteries
91 Holy Week service
92 Pilchards
94 Partly fermented grape juice
96 Word in Daniel 5:25
97 Not heaven
99 News beats
101 President from Virginia
102 Cried, as an owl
104 Lag behind
106 Card game
107 Sensed
108 Notion
109 Catalogue
110 Sight in Sicily
112 Calves (Scot.)
113 Lavish excess affection
114 Insect
115 Lampreys
118 Educational television (abbr.)
120 River in Brazil

PUZZLE 199

ACROSS

1 Garden flower
6 Leftover dish
10 Word with music or food
14 Old German coin
19 Backbone
20 River in France
21 Spicy stew
22 Love, Italian style
23 Star of "Sleeper"
25 Star of "Jezebel"
27 Southern constellation
28 Scoffs
30 Expanded
31 Denomination
32 Education org.
33 Harrow's rival
34 Island of the Carolines
36 Dill plant
38 Short-napped
39 Over again
40 Ablaze
42 Weight allowance
44 American vulture
47 British prison guards
49 Famous evolution trial
53 Crosby-Hope highways
54 Granular snow
55 Jazz pianist Waller
57 Freshet
58 "— Karenina"
59 Roman tetrarch of Galilee
60 A day's march
62 Dies —
63 Rural sound
64 Role for Loretta Young
65 Movie and TV star
67 Leander loved her
68 War god
69 Star of "Cyrano de Bergerac"
75 Taunted
78 Under the weather
81 Seed covering
82 River in France
83 Receded
84 Mass of floating ice
85 Rants
87 Not punctual
88 Property owned absolutely
89 Rows
90 Tilts
92 Role in GWTW
94 A king of Persia
95 River islands
97 Ancient Hebrew weights
98 English pianist
99 Turkish title
102 Ceremony
104 Director (abbr.)
105 Chokes, as a furnace
106 Controversial aircraft
109 Ibsen heroine
111 Pianist Peter
113 A gaseous hydrocarbon
115 Location
116 Star of "Anna Karenina"
119 Co-star of "The Gin Game"
121 Serfs
122 "In the —"
123 Rubber trees
124 Mature
125 Raises upright
126 Winter vehicle
127 Corrupt by time
128 Foundations

DOWN

1 Famous dam
2 Primitive reproductive body
3 County in New York
4 Within: comb. form
5 King, in Spain
6 Not solid
7 Actor Richard —
8 Dagger
9 Star of "The Grapes of Wrath"
10 Weep convulsively
11 Designer Cassini
12 A radical
13 Dormant
14 Small child
15 Chalices
16 Paramour
17 Heath
18 Musical pauses
24 In honor of
26 Pitchers
29 A voyage
33 Grandson of Adam
35 Hold in greater favor
37 Detectives (slang)
39 Egyptian skink
40 Brother of Moses
41 One of the Muses
43 Themes
44 Ill-tempered person
45 Lady Chaplin
46 Zola heroine
47 Tour, in Italy
48 Unpracticed attempt
50 Butterfly fish
51 And others (abbr.)
52 Ooze
54 Of the thigh
56 Fished, in a way
58 Leverets
61 Blundered
64 Ump's relative
66 Spread grass to dry
67 City in Montana
69 Containers
70 Evangelist Roberts
71 Hindu god
72 Wander
73 Penetrate
74 Staggered
75 Star of "The Devil and Miss Jones"
76 Arabian devil
77 Central American tree
78 Holly tree
79 Learning
80 Minus
84 Conifers
86 Agitate
88 Hardy girl
91 Prick painfully
93 Rose's sweetheart
94 Mediterranean vessel
96 Prepares clams, in a way
98 Frank
99 Wrath
100 Furze
101 Sphere of action
103 One of the Flynns
105 Pastimes
106 Body cavity
107 Fashion
108 Camp shelters
110 Biblical name
112 Woodwind
114 O-o feathers
115 Beverage
117 Ninny
118 Strange
120 Fictional dog hero

242

PUZZLE 200

ACROSS

1 Diving bird
5 European finch
10 Wild hogs
15 Falcon, for one
19 Capri is a famous one
20 Valuable violin
21 Interior
22 Famous canal
23 Dross of metal
24 Biblical name
25 River ducks
26 Frog genus
27 Modulated
29 Biblical name
30 Musical group
31 Pierces with tusks
32 Wilson's thrush
34 An article
36 Dress fabric
38 Male turkey
41 Mass: comb. form
42 Lifts for skiers
44 June bug
45 Once called Clay
48 Shore bird
50 Exercised in the gym
52 Allied to the sandpiper
54 Rail birds
55 Heeded
56 One of the Seven Dwarfs
58 Game bird
59 Lath
60 Sound
61 Dyer's vats
63 Danish measure
64 Bird nest collectors
66 Chemical suffix
67 Trap
69 Followers of isms
70 Japanese porgy
71 Eskers
72 Comedian: Jimmy —
76 Girl of song
77 Largest birds
82 Norwegian king
83 Attendant spirit
85 Narrow inlet
86 Counsel (dial.)
87 French painter
89 Patriotic org.
90 The universe
91 Harbinger of spring
92 Kind of written engagement, in law
94 The ancient kingdom of Israel
96 Wooden pins
97 Bishopric
98 The brown kiwi
100 Soothes
101 Fabulous bird
102 Female of the ruff
103 Fragrance
105 Vintage auto
106 Submerges
108 Fore-and-aft rigged vessel
111 Australian bird
113 Biblical word of reproach
115 Aquatic birds
119 Personal: comb. form
120 Ragout of game
121 To daunt (archaic)
123 — fixe
124 Bewail
125 Dress feathers
126 Prickly pear
127 Rich source
128 Letter phase
129 Bird of India
130 Lock of hair
131 Check

DOWN

1 Catalogue
2 Norwegian city
3 Pearl Buck heroine
4 Israeli desert region
5 Weaken
6 Arabian chieftains (var.)
7 Arouse to action
8 Flowering shrub
9 The owl, for one
10 Small heron
11 Unique person
12 Author Nin
13 Burden again
14 Upper classmen (abbr.)
15 Wading bird
16 Sandarac tree
17 Vintner's product
18 New Zealand parrots
28 Attica townships
31 Lassies
33 Consume
35 Foot of an ape
37 Surpass
38 Italian poet
39 Rounded, convex molding
40 Ethical
42 Massenet opera
43 Grasslike plant
45 City in Spain
46 Biblical outcast
47 Goddess of peace
49 Roman statesman
50 Primitive chisels
51 Female antelope
53 Man in Genesis
55 Hurries
57 Describing a certain oriole
60 A long view
61 Cuckoo
62 Lewis Carroll nonsense creature
65 Bar offering
66 Red dye
68 Hindu title of respect
70 Dancer's cymbals
71 Bird medal of Venice
72 Cupolas
73 Characterized by: a suffix
74 Belgian marble
75 Southwest wind
76 Pinnacle of glacier ice
77 European iris
78 Black bird
79 Biblical name
80 Roman official
81 Intelligence
84 Propane
85 Fish-eating bird
88 Small flashlight
90 A wheal
91 Ship hazards
93 Sorrow
95 Game fishes
96 Russian river
99 Turkish city
101 Lariats
103 Range
104 He portrayed Charlie Chan
106 Ending for land or sea
107 Floats on liquid
108 Flightless bird
109 Paradise
110 Row
112 Large bird of Australia
114 God of love
116 Mine entrance
117 Hawaiian goose
118 Appear
120 Without surviving issue (L. abbr.)
122 Overhead railways

244

PUZZLE 201

ACROSS

1 Venetian navigator
8 English navigator
11 Reasoning
16 Lourdes, for one
17 Uncanny
18 Wall described in the Koran
20 Strait, or narrow sea
21 Short fishing line
22 He conquered Peru
24 Steak order
25 Puts in a new container
27 Mexican dollar
29 Asterisk
30 The grampus
31 Horse's fare
32 Author of "Utopia"
33 Business abbr.
34 English navigator
36 Ratio words
37 Golf links
39 Ten: a prefix
40 Commits
42 Lisbon and Malagá
43 Odd jobs
45 Charitable gift
46 Port for 52 Across
47 Othello, for one
48 He conquered Mexico
51 Nobleman
52 Italian navigator
56 An aphid
57 Split
58 Stupid blunder
59 Money of account
60 Minute particle
61 Distributes, as alms
62 Ejects
63 Salute
64 Chess pieces
65 Lyrical ballads
66 Famous Mormon
67 Pastoral
68 City in Australia
70 Lunch and dinner
71 Snuggly
72 River in Italy
73 Confront in defiance
74 Studies
75 Polish city
78 Former Spanish coins
79 Leaping amphibians (var.)
83 French girlfriend
84 Diversions
86 Emporium
87 Pianist Peter
88 Fabulous bird
89 Isaiah (var.)
90 Flaccid
91 Energy unit
92 God of love
94 Hop kiln
95 Ponce —; discoverer of Florida
97 Bark cloth
98 English navigator
100 African antelope
102 Makes payment back
104 Fictional Simon
105 Course or way
106 Lessened
107 Visible sign
108 Goat antelope
109 Flowering water plant

DOWN

1 French explorer
2 English composer
3 Storage compartment
4 Unique person
5 Bony fishes
6 Spanish explorer
7 Leases
8 War god
9 Irish church
10 Marine fishes
11 Slight errors
12 Medley
13 Coin of Oman
14 Levin and Gershwin
15 French navigator
16 Israeli plain
19 French writer
20 Cross, in Milan
23 Killer whales
26 Butter servings
28 Blunders
32 Mental defective
35 Watchdog of the seven Sleepers
36 Doctrines
37 City in Panama
38 French schools
39 College bedroom
41 Rubber trees
42 Removes the rind
44 Period of time
46 Surfaces
47 May or June
48 South African fox
49 Made choice
50 River in France
51 Bottom of a ship's hull
52 Prices
53 Authorized assembly
54 Wild sheep of India
55 Girl of song
57 Last movement of a sonata
58 Construct
61 Actions
62 Bradley and Sharif
63 English navigator
65 Garment for Indira
66 Some are eared
67 A dwarf
69 Spend time in idleness
70 Pithy
71 Early Egyptian
73 Scolders
74 Below a sergeant
75 Challenger
76 Without a sense of responsibility
77 French explorer
78 British polar explorer
79 Harness part
80 Charges with gas
81 Arranged in folds
82 Fountain drinks
85 Female peacock
86 Growth on plants
90 Slow, in music
93 State flower of Utah
94 Curved molding
95 They are related to the Manchus
96 Mountain in Moab
97 Giant armadillo (var.)
99 Vex
101 Love (Scot.)
103 Nocturnal creature

PUZZLE 202

ACROSS

1 Defense org.
5 Opera treats
10 Lively dance
15 Eskers
19 God of love
20 Devilfish
21 Worship
22 Colombian seaport
23 Noted boxer
25 Noted golfer
27 Upward curve of ship's planking
28 Inquires
29 Pen point
31 Wife of Ramachandra
32 Used in jewelry
33 Headlands
35 Yields
37 Genus of ferns
39 Mistreated
41 Lab vessels
43 Lower or under
46 Legal wrongs
47 Crescent-shaped figure
48 Denomination
50 Cubic meter
51 French novelist
52 Impression
53 Indochinese kingdom
55 Son of Seth
56 Philippine Negrito
57 Won out over
59 Cylindrical and tapered
61 Follower of an ism
62 Methods
64 Bellows
66 Naval construction men
68 Wrath
69 Miss Farrow
70 Start for fix or text
71 The right of primogeniture
75 Divisions of a school year
77 Skunk
81 Before
82 A feeling of hatred
84 Like a sponge
86 City in Oklahoma
87 Catalogue
89 Social rebuff
90 Shed hair
91 Ancient Syria
92 Fundamental principles
94 European river
96 Storage tower
97 Certain reproduction
98 Anoints (archaic)
100 Raise
102 Lack of color
103 Paddled
105 Suppose
106 Miss Bernhardt
107 Stitch
109 Genus of cetaceans
111 California fort
112 Hebrides island
113 Time period
116 West Point football star
119 U.S. Olympic star
122 Japanese aborigine (var.)
123 Growing out
124 Portrayer of Charlie Chan
125 Concerning
126 Soviet countries (abbr.)
127 Chest sounds
128 City in Ohio
129 Peter or Ivan

DOWN

1 Inferior horses
2 So be it
3 He played "The All American"
4 Crude metal
5 Entertained
6 Orderly arrangements
7 Hostels
8 Consumed
9 Short music drama
10 They chew the fat
11 Commotion
12 Tennis strokes
13 Scope of activity
14 Fictional Place
15 Indian
16 Norwegian Olympic skater
17 Nautical term
18 Degenerate in idleness
24 Records
26 Fatigues
30 Artificial language
34 Winegrowing region of Italy
35 The core
36 Stone pillars
38 Diminutive suffix
39 Burden-bearer
40 Spoils of war
41 Dwarf
42 Cicatrix
44 Appearing eaten
45 Takes five
47 Minus
49 Pedal digits
52 Humbles
54 Go on a date
57 Name in baseball
58 Cupolas
59 Vagrant
60 Noblemen
63 Pedro's uncle
65 Melody
67 Insect
71 Australian soprano
72 Suffix denoting occupation
73 U.S. Olympic star
74 Ceramic square
75 Black gum
76 Metamere
77 Active sport
78 U.S. Olympic skater
79 "A Bell for --"
80 More docile
83 Manufactured
85 Part
88 A tissue
91 — breve
93 Finch
95 Lies at rest
96 Child's delight
97 Jeweler's weight
99 Dispatcher
101 Vigor (Scot.)
102 Dish having soaked breadcrumbs
104 Ancient Italian goddess
106 Sleep: comb. form
107 Indochinese language
108 Ancient Greek country
110 Grandparental
112 A sea Dyak
114 New Zealand tree
115 Hebrew instrument
117 And not
118 Native of: a suffix
120 Madrid cheer
121 Stetson

PUZZLE 203

ACROSS

1 Struck
5 Strong fiber
9 Cabbage salad
13 Kind of race
17 Extinct Bahama Indian
18 Armadillo
19 Comfort
20 Bury
22 They (Fr. fem.)
23 Impute a wrong motive to
25 Mouthlike opening
26 Drinks mid-morning coffee
28 Detracts from
30 Overhead railways
31 Scheme
32 Murder fine (Scot.)
34 Distance measure
35 Abstract being
36 Wild garlic
37 Parade feature
38 Containers
41 Revolve
44 New Jersey city
46 Declares
50 U.S. president
51 By way of
52 Hastened
54 Drudge
55 A fuel
56 Indited

59 Regan's father
61 Abyssinian weight
62 Land measure
63 Soft job
65 Visionaries
67 Chemical compound
69 Wear away
71 Washes
72 Accomplished
75 Poet's evening
77 Make lace
80 New Zealand tree
81 Crude metals
83 The "lily maid of Astolat"
84 Ill-humor
85 Goddess of peace
87 Bristle
89 One of the "Little Women"
90 Greek epic poet
91 Most painful
93 Households
96 Whalebone
97 Hwys.
99 Relating to form
100 Rave
101 Roman bronze
104 Cereal grasses
106 Trouble
107 Office fixture
108 A quid (slang)
111 Occur

114 Carry off the prize
117 A hike
118 Assume a definite form
120 French historian
121 Open the package
122 French islands
123 Presently
124 Obliterate
125 Vend
126 Scottish land tax
127 A fruit
128 A ration for the poor

DOWN

1 Pacific coast shrub
2 Does a farm chore
3 Arrow poison
4 Drunkards
5 Ball park denizen
6 Aside
7 Japanese beverage
8 Molasses
9 Son of Noah (var.)
10 Cafe au —
11 Its capital is Shillong
12 Waistcoat (dial. var.)
13 Disagrees
14 Pilaster

15 City in Vermont
16 Man's name
17 Head (Fr.)
21 Beams
24 City in Ohio
27 Auk genus
29 Ancient Greek city
33 Solemn vow
36 Role for Angela Lansbury
37 French writer
38 Labor
40 Daughter of Herodias
41 Biblical word of reproach
42 Fragrance
43 Resemble
44 Prong
45 Require
47 Is patient
48 Always
49 Defeats, at bridge
51 Overlays with wood
53 Word of endearment
56 Kind of pony
57 River in France
58 Herd
60 English author
63 Thus (L.)
64 Noble (Ger.)
66 Salutation
68 Nastier
70 Kind of paint

72 Sister of Ares
73 Gambling game
74 Suppose
76 Cravats
78 To the sheltered side
79 Sea bird
82 Check
84 Run away
86 Kind of legal bar
88 Wild ox
90 Had a longing for
92 River duck
94 Mine entrances
95 Surnamed "the chaste"
96 Smash
98 Radio interference
100 Product of pine tar
101 Aleutian Island
102 Merits
103 Ray
105 Fish property
107 Railroad station
108 Artificial channel
109 Official decree
110 English sand hill
112 Man's name
113 Supplements
115 Japanese writing
116 Food fish
119 Letter

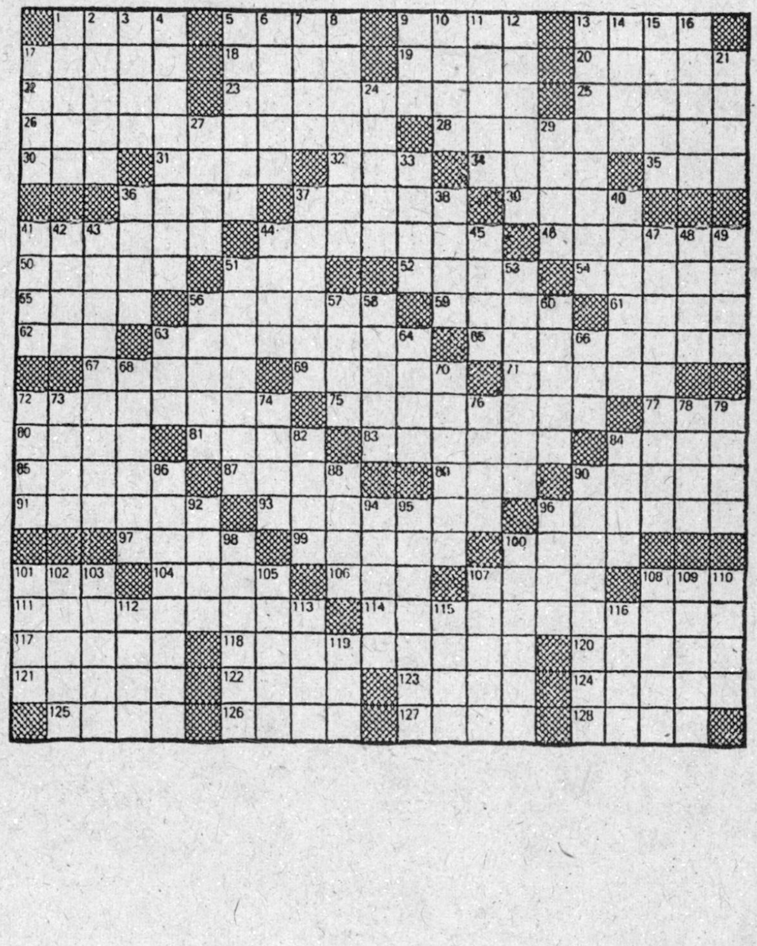

PUZZLE 204

ACROSS

1 To ponder
6 Panama gum tree
10 He invented the "six-shooter"
14 Boy Scout badge
19 Firearm
20 Unruly tumult
21 Buckeye State
22 Loos or Louise
23 Proffer
24 Heroine of "Born Free"
25 Wise man
26 Bovine milk gland
27 A step
28 Born
29 Valuable violin (short.)
30 Prophets
31 West Indian wild dog
34 Expiated
36 Babylonian god
39 Insect eggs
40 The turmeric
42 River to the Elbe
43 Haggard novel
46 Obtain by devious methods
48 Light, strong wood
50 Mexican blankets
52 Supposed
53 He invented a crank-type machine gun
55 Straightforward
56 Appraiser
57 Melody
58 French illustrator
60 Ipso —
61 Ass (Ger.)
62 Accented syllables (Pros.)
63 Kind of paint
65 Mountain (South Africa)
66 Heron
68 Climbing plants
70 Past
73 "The Scourge of God"
76 Retinue
78 Jones and Sawyer
82 A prime mover
84 Social climber
85 Islands (Fr.)
86 Name of a popular knife of the West
87 Noah's landing place
89 Chatters
91 Unclothe
92 Infernal
94 Customs
95 Fuchsin
96 Pub order
97 American general
99 Treat hides
100 Domestic pigeon
101 Compass reading
102 Peaceful
104 United
107 Ancient tribe of Britons
110 Growing out
112 High, in music
113 Raves
117 Husks of grains
118 Israeli seaport
119 Angle between branch and stem
120 Characteristic
121 Atelier feature
122 Head (Fr.)
123 Dimensions
124 Johanna Spyri heroine
125 Cubic meter
126 Paradise
127 City in Iowa
128 Felix or Luther

DOWN

1 Abbr. used in business
2 A fissure
3 Teutonic legendary hero
4 Oily acid
5 Short-barreled, large-caliber pistol
6 Having a scalloped margin
7 Commercial vessels
8 Knotty problem
9 Indonesian of Mindanao
10 Price
11 He wrote "A Rage to Live"
12 To bandage
13 Machine shop needs
14 Weapon invented by two German brothers
15 Concluded
16 Carnival attraction
17 Roman road
18 Sailors
29 Short fishing line
32 Gentle
33 Declaims
35 Require
36 Before (Naut.)
37 East Indian palm trees
38 Combine
41 Stage whisper
43 Small spot
44 Hundred: comb. form
45 Plug up
47 Anoint (archaic)
48 Poison
49 Presently
51 Constellation
53 Weather word
54 Sauces for meat
57 Makes weight allowance
59 Discharges
62 Skill
64 Chemical suffix
67 Basic weapon for U.S. soldiers in WWII
69 Kitchen appliance
70 Biblical name
71 Goat antelope
72 Giant grass
74 Friable soil
75 Head of a monastery
76 Genus of the wild pink
77 Rubber trees
79 American Olympic star
80 Hazes
81 Bristles
83 Money of account
86 Gargantuan German cannon
88 Become weary
90 A pair
91 Pub missile
93 Wedge-shaped
95 Cloaks
98 Chopped finely
100 Formerly British Honduras
102 Conclude
103 Bill of fare
105 He created the first modern machine gun
106 Challenged
107 Popular desserts
108 Converse
109 Comfort
111 Numerical suffix
114 Brad, for one
115 To surge
116 Agitate
119 Neat — pin

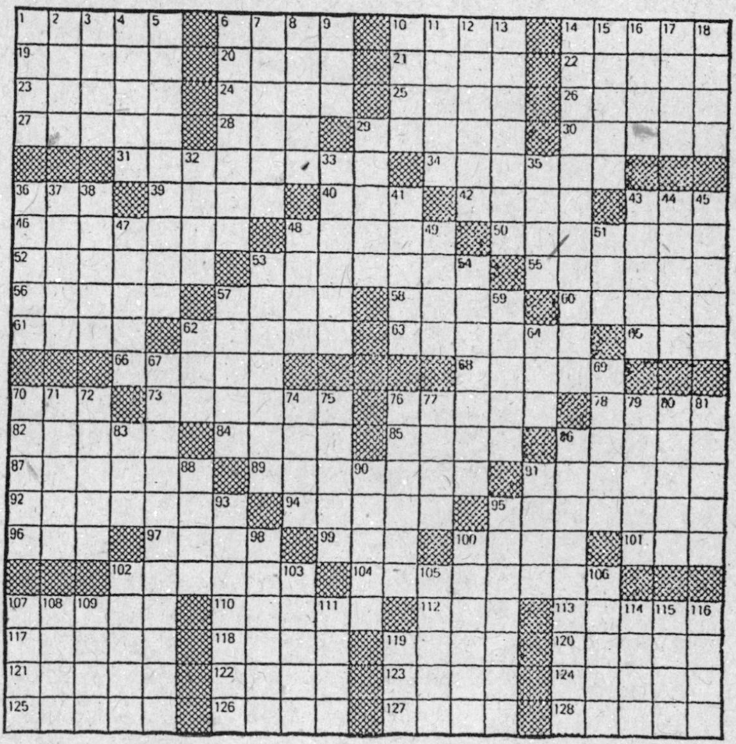

PUZZLE 205

ACROSS

1 Formerly Belgian Congo
6 Boxes
11 Split
16 Virgin
17 Abnormal growth
18 Beast
20 Malayan musical instrument
21 Fragrant oleoresin
22 Violent surfs of Guinea coast
24 Biblical name
25 Beer mug
27 The "lily maid of Astolat"
29 Family of Negro tribes
30 Cousin of USSR
32 Break suddenly
33 British composer
34 Second son of Adam
36 Wheeled vehicles
37 Author Gardner
39 Unexpected obstacle
40 Deceitful cunning
41 Injure by fire
43 Hardwood trees
45 Swamp
46 Lady Chaplin
48 Drug-yielding plant
49 Island of the West Indies
50 Formerly Bechuanaland
54 Satisfied
56 Ponder
59 Epic poetry
60 Tree cobra
62 Hebrew dry measures
64 Assam silkworm
65 Not pos.
66 Norwegian statesman
67 Black gold
68 Short-napped
69 Formerly Persia
71 Small particles
73 Magna —
75 Withered
76 Study of noses
78 Chinese pagoda
80 Of mother and father
82 To modify
83 Formerly Edo
85 Steak order
86 Take out
89 Large drawing rooms
91 Formerly Nyasaland
96 Anoint (archaic)
96 Window section
97 Son of Adam
99 More cunning
100 Young girl
101 Ruth's husband
102 God (Lat.)
104 Pintail duck
105 WWII area
106 Petty prince
108 Formerly Northern Rhodesia
110 Commotion
111 Give a place to
113 Biblical name
115 Holy City of the Hindus
117 Styx ferryman
118 Wrathful
119 Cheap
120 Female figure in prayer posture
121 Chief Teutonic gods
122 Buddy and Max

DOWN

1 Russian hors d'oeuvre
2 Trouble
3 Wedding promises
4 Descartes, et al.
5 Any mechanical tool
6 Church spires
7 Haul
8 Soul (Fr.)
9 City of seven hills
10 Formerly Ceylon
11 Tidying the lawn
12 Senseless
13 Odious
14 Uncle (dial.)
15 Formerly South West Africa
16 Of memory
19 Tags
20 Semites
23 Shoe parts
26 Black tern
28 Brazilian macaws
31 Throw again
34 A salt of auric acid
36 Display
38 Dropsy
39 A votre —
40 Large desert
42 Hindu charitable gift
44 United
45 Drinking vessels
47 Likeness
49 Substance used in dyes
50 Formerly Dahomey
51 Thais or Aida
52 Roman garments
53 Friendship
55 Bird sound
56 Decree
57 Coronet
58 Atelier feature
61 Spelling contest
63 Kentucky bluegrass
70 Fictional books
71 British statesman
72 Fur piece
73 Keys or cays
74 Ancient country
76 Short fishing lines
77 Tardy
79 Hungarian liquid measure
81 Periods of time
83 Formerly Tanganyika and Zanzibar
84 Timid swain?
86 Evans and Robertson
87 Related on the mother's side
88 Formerly Basutoland
89 European river
90 Check
92 South American food fishes
93 Garden tool
94 Florentine iris (obs.)
96 Mighty
98 Tumult
101 Conductor's wand
103 City near Florence
106 Poet Teasdale
107 French father
108 Bonnet monkey
109 Peruvian Indian
112 Now defunct union (abbr.)
114 Stocking, in France
116 Air: comb. form

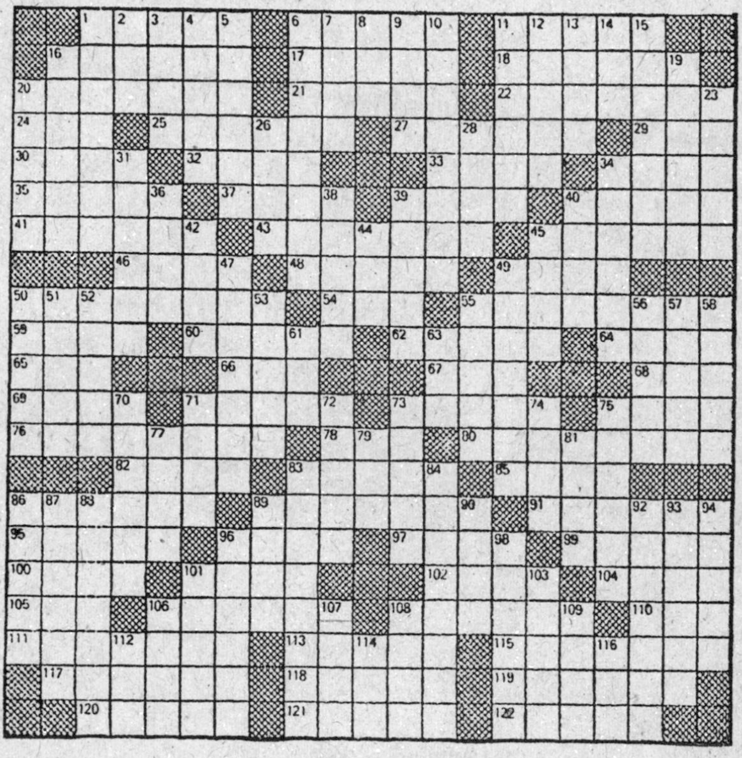

PUZZLE 206

ACROSS

1 Navigate
5 Capital of Oregon
10 Alabama city
15 Tolerable
19 Ballerina's skirt
20 Sphere of action
21 Mountain nymph
22 Cavity
23 Solar disk
24 Family of Negro tribes
25 Climbing plant
26 Man in Genesis
27 One of the Society Islands
29 Festival: comb. form
31 Samoan town
33 So long
34 Preserves in brine
36 Kind of tide
37 Ledger listings
40 Pondered
42 Fence steps
46 Lewis Carroll heroine
47 Labor org.
48 Indian, for one
50 Slyly sarcastic
51 Role for Robert Stack
52 A plait
54 Heating vessels
56 European kite
57 I love (L.)
58 French city
60 English hymn writer
62 Chalice
63 British social gathering
65 Customs
67 French dance
69 Indian
70 Malodorous
71 Zola heroine
72 Kind of drum
75 Yields
76 Table game
80 Edible tuber
81 Make second offer
83 A relaxing (Fr.)
85 Patriotic org.
86 Girl's name
88 Stiffness
90 Leases
91 "In Spain they say —"
92 Secluded valleys
94 Discloses
96 Anglo-Saxon letter
97 Inexpensive
98 Fur pieces
100 Allowances
102 Coils
103 Girl's name
105 Stage direction
106 Bandman Artie
107 "Chitty, Chitty, —"
111 King, in France
112 Mustard pickles
116 Word in Mark 15:34
117 Snare anew
119 Canadian physician
121 English river
122 Collar or jacket
123 Puff up
124 Useful
125 Scorch
126 Chinese secret society
127 Stitched
128 Pagan deities
129 Serf, once

DOWN

1 Spontaneous attempt
2 Self: comb. form
3 Roman road
4 Madmen
5 Wooden shoes
6 Palm cockatoo
7 Russian river
8 Suffix forming adjectives
9 Member of a secret society in Kenya
10 Highest point
11 Son of God
12 Vault
13 Grand — Island, Canada
14 Maxims
15 Looking for bargains
16 Lady Chaplin
17 Dross
18 Wine: comb. form
28 Moderate
30 Actor: — Ray
32 Food for horses
34 Impassive
35 Boiled (archaic)
37 Wynter and Andrews
38 Oleoresin
39 Ox-like quadruped
40 Cant of thieves
41 Borge, et al.
43 Garden shrub
44 Dropsy
45 Style of auto
47 Goddess of peace
49 Seize roughly
52 Leather scourer
53 Having a cupola
55 Cutting lines (Geom.)
58 American capitalist
59 Observed
61 Scope
64 Obtained
66 Stair part
68 Forty winks
70 Men's hats
71 Crucial baseball inning
72 Leaping amphibians
73 Group of eight
74 Daughter of Danny Thomas
75 Corona, for one
76 Awaits settlement
77 Willow
78 Of the nose
79 Valises (colloq.)
82 Baby's need
84 Early years
87 Asserting
89 Replied
91 Display box
93 Slav
95 Farm building
97 Chew (vulgar)
99 Traps
101 "In France they say —"
102 Harlots
104 Anoint (archaic)
106 Outer covering
107 Root vegetable
108 Choir section
109 Midday
110 Chew upon
112 Muse of history
113 Hastens
114 Algerian seaport
115 "The Way We —"
118 Nice season
120 Degree in theology

Puzzle 4

```
SCAB  CRIST
NOTE  RACHEL
IRON  INHALE
PALERMO  PEG
ELL EEN ERA
    SEA FLAT
STEED  WAYNE
ARAL  WAD
NOS SIR POI
TUT  HEPBURN
ONEMAN  ELAN
SCRAPE  ESTE
ENTER  PEER
```

Puzzle 1

```
PLAT  LARS
LORE  ORATOR
ANTA  BEHAVE
YES SEA TEG
  AGED  PERU
DINAR  ROLL
INDIA  SOFIA
SECT  ENTER
ERRS  HIGH
ATA PER ELI
SIFTED  LAIR
EATING  ARNO
SATE  ETON
```

Puzzle 5

```
PATE  SMITH
AVAL  WASHER
RELY  ADHERE
IRK ARE MEG
STORED  META
FAR  ARIL
PATTY  CIRCE
ACHE  ANY
ICED  CREWEL
SET DRY ILI
ADOREE  EDIT
NEWEST  ROTE
SNAKE  EWER
```

Puzzle 2

```
CLOD  STROP
HIDE  PROPEL
AMON  ROWENA
RAREBIT  RAT
    RESTATE
MEIR  ATEN
CRATE  FROST
AERO  PIER
EVINCED
SIE  ANOMALY
ASTERN  ARIA
RETIRE  SELL
DARED  HATE
```

Puzzle 3

```
OHNE  INCITE
DEEP  SEAMEN
ERSE  SENILE
ROSEBUD  TER
    REY  ARG
  ROAD  STAY
TENT  SEEN
DOME  SEED
ARI  DEE
NON  ORMANDY
INDORE  TARA
STEPIN  OVAL
HORACE  PETE
```

Puzzle 6

```
CROW  BRACED
RENO  REPOSE
ADEN  ASTUTE
WEB IZE NEP
LEO SET TEL
MYMAN  ARMY
SOY  SNY
BABA  SINCE
AVO PAL ORT
HAS ALL URE
ALTONA  ISAR
MOONED  LINN
ANNALS  ANTE
```

258

Puzzle 11

```
MAMA TRACTS
ALOP REMORA
LIVE ENAMEL
TEE RAT EMU
ANIMATE TOT
   NAVY POLE
SHARE SYNOD
HECK MORO
URI BARETTA
DOR RIT HID
DICTUM HIND
ENLACE INGE
REELED EGER
```

Puzzle 7

```
SMUT MAS
CAPRA AMISS
ANTIC SINCE
REO TAA CID
  NAOMI LEA
ROSINA CANT
OVINE PRICE
TENT SEERED
ARC TIDAL
TAL HAD ETA
ETAPE LOWER
DEIST ELITE
 RIIA ASEA
```

Puzzle 8

```
SETA ALIAS
TAHR SAMITE
AGEE STOLEN
MEL REH VET
PROCURE ETA
 NAST DREI
TRESS NOBEL
RARE MENU
IVA MANILOW
BIN OLE LAR
ANGORA SETI
LEERED STET
 RELY ESNE
```

Puzzle 12

```
SAGO MINAR
CLOD SEVERE
ATTA ALEXIS
RAH DUE TST
PRELATE TIE
  WIRE FOND
CHEE WING
SHOD HALO
TIL LYNETTE
AME OPT HAN
REHIRE LIST
ERODED ANTE
SAGAN EGER
```

Puzzle 9

```
SOFA ADAGE
IRON MORONS
DALI INTOTO
ELL DEN URN
 OPINE TEA
 SWISS MOAT
SWANK LIFTA
COCK NASTY
ROO PORCH
ANU AND EVA
PIRATE SWIM
ENSATE EASE
GELIID RYAN
```

Puzzle 13

```
MADE SPACES
IRON PINOLE
NEWT APEMEN
ANN ARE EGO
RATTLER TAR
  HOLD DONA
 METE LIAT
SAME MARC
TRI PATTERN
OLD ITE NEE
WIDGET ATAP
ENLACE BETA
DEEPER ARAL
```

Puzzle 10

```
CANE PIO
HOOP ARTIST
ANTI GOOBER
TEA PAN ERE
 BOONS GIA
CRIMES ETAT
RETEM SMOTE
IVAN GUIDED
MEL TOSTI
ERI HIA FAT
ASKOUT AFRO
NEEDLE REEL
 DER ARAL
```

Puzzle 14

```
BALE CLASH
ABET HUSHED
LOVEFORSALE
IRE ASI TOT
 TRACED NIE
  TEN LESS
SPLIT CARET
TRAP TAN
ROT TALKER
OPT AME ROA
DOITUPBROWN
ESCAPE EDEN
EELER PELE
```

Puzzle 17

```
BOAR ODIST
ALBA LOTTE
BABESINARMS
AYE AVE APT
    STE AFOR
COTTER TIRO
AIRED MONAD
BLIP DANGLE
RIAS ARE
ANN ANI HAO
LEGSDIAMOND
SLIDE ANTE
SEGAL REAR
```

Puzzle 15

```
HAHA BRIES
AGES EARLET
IRAK SLAYER
LEV PIE SRI
SEERED DIET
NICE EASE
ROCK MANS
LANE CALE
EDER ONTIME
TIA PRY EEL
HARDEN SLAG
ENTIRE ADDA
THEIR YSER
```

Puzzle 18

```
SLAT CANT
LOLA ONEACT
ARAL ATTILA
MOSCATO LIP
   WINSOME
SLIME ARAR
PACED CRETE
AVES AIDED
NEWSMEN
KRA ORATORY
ENTIRE ERIE
DEEDED ANTA
ROSE REAR
```

Puzzle 16

```
RACK PRE
ALOE LANCER
ZOLA INTONE
END WAG ODD
DESTINE LEA
 TINT THAN
PRONE CHART
HERE SOON
ASA SALUDOS
SIG PUT LUM
EDENIC CUTE
DESIRE OKRA
PER PEER
```

Puzzle 19

```
RAJA CHAFED
ABET REPOSE
DORE ALERTS
ADO AVA DUE
REMADE AMAR
 EVEN TART
 SKIN BODY
MAJA RENO
OMEN ALEXIS
DOR VIA FRA
EVOKED MOAT
SAMITE ARTA
TREMOR EDEN
```

Puzzle 23

```
CHIN DIETER
LONE INROME
ANTE SEABED
RAH CUR ERR
ANIMIST OSE
  SITE EROS
SAONE FINNS
ABUT HERO
LAR TOLETAN
ALL HOT TIO
MOILED COST
INFUSE ABLE
SEEMED REED
```

Puzzle 20

```
CALI DELETE
ADAN ONEMAN
ROCKANDROLL
ORE ADE TEA
METERED INC
  TOR TOTE
TORN LENS
RARE BIN
ARE SANTAFE
VAS INE BAX
INTHEGROOVE
STEEVE ODOR
HOSTED PERT
```

Puzzle 21

```
PAPA BATHE
AMEN EGOIST
SAND FIESTA
TIN TOL GOG
ANYMORE INE
  SIRE GRIN
CREME SALAD
HERE GOLF
AVE COTERIE
SIN LOS IRA
EVADED ODER
RADIAL LANE
LEERY DYED
```

Puzzle 22

```
COTTE CLEW
ARAD RATITE
PESO OPENER
RAT BUS GER
ADIPOSE ETA
  NILE ADEN
BEGET RIVET
ENDS SARI
ATE REJECTS
RIF ORA TIN
ICEAGE NONO
TEAMEN ERGO
TARE EYED
```

Puzzle 24

```
ABBE RENOIR
CURL AROUSE
TRIM CANTON
ERN SIS OLE
DOGGONE EAG
TALE NOTE
SCOPE MINED
TORE FINE
ONE CANASTA
ODA HIT MET
POSTAL LINT
ELOISE ANSA
DENTED EDER
```

Puzzle 25

```
RAFT SPACE
CSLO NOLOSS
AHEM INFUSE
SEA APT NET
TRIPLE TNT
NEER DICE
CLOSE BONER
RENT GONG
AVE REINER
YES TAR OLA
OREGON TSAR
NEARED RETE
TRADE YSER
```

Puzzle 26

```
CORE SOBER
OMEGA TRACE
MINORLEAGUE
OTT RILL
GIBE LIAW
SHEAVE FINE
MASTERPLANS
ELSE ARARAT
WOE STAG
TEEN SIIA
SECONDCLASS
ATHOS EAGLE
GAITE DEEM
```

Puzzle 27

```
BASE DAN
AMID EDISTO
DORE RATHER
GUL BIG ORR
EROSIVE ORE
INRE STER
SANER PETTY
ERSE MACH
RIT SUTTERS
ESE TRE BAT
NEATER LUNE
ANKARA ALGA
REY BLED
```

Puzzle 30

```
IRON SASH
DANE ELIAS
LITTLEEGYPT
EDO AIR SAR
SPLINT ERE
ERG LESS
CARED AIDES
ADAR HON
ROT PARANA
ORT ANT ART
BELLYDANCER
DEANE ARNO
REEL BEAD
```

Puzzle 28

```
MAUL MASS
ABRA EDIITH
GOBI MARRED
IIVA LOG ERE
CENSURE EER
GORY TAR
ACUTE LEFTY
CHE SERI
HOR CHARGES
ERI RIP HAT
SULLEN ETRE
SLATE FELL
AYER TREE
```

Puzzle 31

```
LABEL SCOUT
OLIVE PASSE
BAKEDALASKA
ONE FIN
WATT NET
ATEASE AERO
WELSHRABBIT
ATOP MALONE
YEN MARE
SAT LEI
FRENCHTOAST
RIIVAL ARISE
ADAGE TOTEM
```

Puzzle 29

```
AMARA TRASH
COVET HANOI
THEBLUENILE
ORR ERR SER
SAGENE
REFUSE OTTO
ODIIST RIITES
TORA BESETS
ENERGY
ASS VIA ALF
SWANEERIVER
TALER DRONE
INEPT SENSE
```

Puzzle 32

```
CAMP ADOBE
AMUR RAKIISH
ROSY ORELSE
ELI OUT LEA
DECORS PINT
AINE LACE
MILLE DARED
ONCE POND
LEHR RITTER
ERA DON ARA
STIRUP TBAR
TIRADE ELSE
ASTER DEER
```

Puzzle 33

```
THIN   ARIA
HONOR CONGA
ENTRE UNFIT
REH MOT ITO
EYESORE NAN
  DIVA FETE
STOLE LIFER
CALL   TINE
ALD PINNACE
LAR RAG TON
ARUBA ETHAN
RIMED REESE
 ASTO  ARTA
```

Puzzle 37

```
SHAM   COOP
HERR  ONEAL
ARNE GARLIC
GOODBET  EVA
    ONE FEN
CACHET CANA
ASHER RACER
SPEW  REMEDY
PIE   SOT
ERR AWESOME
REFUTE  LEER
 DUPIN ASTI
 LANA  BEAN
```

Puzzle 34

```
BOTH   START
ASHER  LAGER
STARE  AGATE
HIT CAN IRA
 ASSENT NAT
  TENT LACY
  CHAT CENT
CHER   POND
HAL   MORTAL
ERI IDO GET
ELMAN NIATA
SEINE ARION
ESTER  ENNA
```

Puzzle 38

```
MARAT  LALA
IRONY AGING
MASTROIANNI
ELY AIT GUL
   ONLY ELD
 HINNY ORLE
CANDY FRIED
ARTE  PINED
EDE   HONE
SER OLA ROT
ANNAMAGNANI
REEVE LANCE
DEER  ENTER
```

Puzzle 35

```
BAKE    CAT
ANITA ORATE
RISER MAKER
OSS TIE ERR
NEATEST ORA
 NORM  ANON
REDDY SNERD
EMMY   PAIS
MIA WELLFED
ILK RIA ARI
SIEPI MANIA
SAUTE INCAN
 PAR   TYNE
```

Puzzle 39

```
AMAH  AMASS
VANE DISMAS
ARAR ONSALE
LAYBARE LIT
   HER LET
SNOOD  TONE
PEONY SINCE
ANSA  CAREY
UTE   SAN
SID ARDMORE
ENISLE ALAN
DEVIISE SENN
LEPER  TATA
```

Puzzle 36

```
ROAR   WHOM
ELSE  HERAT
SITE IMARET
TOOLATE GAR
 DEN    ATA
STRAIN ARID
TRENT CREME
RADA DIETER
ACH   MATT
SHE ORESTES
SEASON HOLE
ARISE  ARIA
TAEL   MEAT
```

Puzzle 40

```
PAPE   ABBES
IDOL  ORELSE
COWL  PETITE
ORE HIT  NUT
TERRENE  DAH
 FARE  MARE
 SAID  GAMY
LOIN  TOMB
ALL MORAINE
TAU ANY  TAW
ERRANT  SITE
NIELLO  HOAR
TASTY  ONLY
```

Puzzle 43

```
HOWE    ASS
ADANA  PACT
HELEN AMARA
ARK GAR  REG
 ISLET  LAR
CENTER  BEDE
ALGER  TITLE
REPP  MILLED
AVA  BELLE
TAP ELL  TOG
STERN  ESTER
 ERIN  REESE
 SAY   TREY
```

Puzzle 41

```
MALAR  CRUST
ARETE  LANCE
NOVASCOTIIAN
OSE TON  ALA
NEE OLE  TEN
 ART  CENT
CURE  CASE
GONE  LAY
AND CAM  SIT
USA ORE  ORA
GOTOHALIIFAX
ELEVE  ORATE
SEDAN  TIRED
```

Puzzle 44

```
RISK   GOTAT
ASTER  ELUDE
REATA  TERMS
ERN VIA  NIT
REDMEN  AIRA
 SALE  GNAT
PRESS  PEALE
LENS  MANN
ESTE ATTACH
ATI PET  LOA
SINAI  ELAND
EVENT  DIRGE
DELAY   AMOS
```

Puzzle 42

```
RATE  ADAGE
OMIT  SENILE
POME  SNIVEL
ERE DON  EVA
DEANERY  NAT
 FEET  FETE
ROTOR  COWED
EVEN  COOL
BER CHALICE
ART HOT  FAR
TAILOR  HEIR
ELMIRA  ETRE
 LEVEL  WOOD
```

Puzzle 45

```
CLUB  STRAND
RIPE  ARABIA
AMID  LOMOND
BAN DEW  VEE
 TEE   ERE
COHEN  LOOSE
OVER   UNIT
TACIT  STERE
 LEE   LES
ADO ROY  HAD
LAUDED  PERE
INDITE  RAIN
FESTER  EDDY
```

```
DATA TRACT
ULAN RATHER
MIKE ADHERE
ACE ANI CRI
SERPICO KAN
  EIRE MICE
NESTS LINER
OLIO COLA
NED COLONNA
AGE AAL DOM
MANNIX SORB
ENCORE RUSE
 TENOR ITER
```

```
CLAY SPEAR
RIDE WILDER
OMAN INLOVE
PIN APT REP
 TABLE LINE
  RED INGA
SALEM BAGEL
EGAD TAN
NERA ENACT
ALI SEE HOR
TESTED WINO
ESSENE ACTA
 SANDE GOON
```

```
ASHER ISLIP
CHASE NOONE
RAVED STOUT
ERE HOE KRA
 DIVERT FIR
 TEAR BOND
 CAID BORG
CALL MEOW
OIL CENTAL
ORO ROA RAM
LEVEE RIDGE
INERT ENTER
TERNE SNORE
```

```
CLEE ONA
LEAR RONDEL
ONCE ATTUNE
DAH ATE ETA
 DOPED LEN
CHASED MIND
HEWED MONTE
ARNE SETTER
ROI HEATH
MID ACT ERR
ENISLE ASEA
REEKED DUNK
 IRE ANTE
```

```
SITE BEAT
LAHR ANTHEM
OGEE CATENA
TOM DOR MAN
 OPINE OCA
SPOOKS MOTT
TENSE DONEE
ERIE RESIDE
ASS RENTS
MOB AMY DAM
ENLACE ROBE
DAUBED EWER
 EERY ANTE
```

```
BABE CREST
ADEN LATTER
SAND INHALE
EGG LEG TEL
SEALANE ERA
 LENT STAT
SALAD HERNE
ARAN DOMO
NIN SERIOUS
TEC OMA PRO
OTELLO REIN
STRAIT ORAN
ASIDE ASHY
```

```
ETRE LAWS
LEADS OTHER
ANCON STARE
NOE IKE TIC
DROPPER SAT
 NEED OTTO
CHEER ETHER
RASP BRIE
ELM MARCHER
ABO ODA ULE
SETON NORMA
ERODE TIRED
TREY LYRE
```

```
SHOE SCAR
HOUR TAROT
ARTA ANKARA
DAH PRO RED
  ELEVE LAM
SPRITE TITII
PRONE FAKER
REDO RECEDE
ASH SENTA
ITE HIT LAR
NORMAN MIRO
 NOONE IONA
 DEER ANON
```

```
DOTED LAVER
ISERE ABIDE
SIRES RECUT
HER COG ICI
 ROTATE OAR
 RINE LUTE
RESET FUSEE
ELMS DISC
LAI DENTIL
ATT AYE ROB
TITAN SACRE
EVERT SALEM
DENSE ELENA
```

```
ROSE BASHED
AVID AVIIATE
METE SERVAL
PRO EER ETE
 NAG TEA
MITRE SCAN
OTHER STORE
TEEN COMET
 FAT ACE
ALE HIT DEN
TENDER DODO
INCOME EWER
PEERED ANNE
```

```
DRAB FACED
AULA MORALE
DILLPICKLES
ONE ANA IVE
 GRAVEL BAR
 MAR WATT
SATIN LINES
ACRE SON
LEI PADDLE
UTE INE IRE
TOSSEDSALAD
ENTITY ELSE
SEEDY SEER
```

```
LACK SCARP
ASHE BEARER
BOON ORNATE
ONO FOG BAM
RECLINE IRE
 HOLE LADD
COOL CONS
CHOP WORN
LOT MANNISH
ORR EIN GNU
STAIRS SHAG
ELICIT ETRE
TENET ISER
```

```
MARIS ARID
ARENA BEGET
JOHNNYBENCH
OMA JOE ORR
RAB ORY BIO
 ASE ALEN
SPARE SWEDE
CORK FEE
ALB HER LIP
LEI ALI IDA
ENTERTAINER
STEAD TREAT
ARTY EARLY
```

Puzzle 59

```
PIPE  PELU
ORAL AVENGE
LISI TANDEM
ESS MED ETA
 ATONE  RON
MOGULS  NOVA
AVERT BENET
LEON SEVERE
ARF  SHOES
BAA ION HAP
AGREED MANE
REMAND ENNA
 STAY ODER
```

Puzzle 60

```
HOOF  GRIST
OVER RATTER
PETEROTOOLE
 NATIVE PEG
   PEL OVA
SELLER EVIL
EVIAN REESE
RIVE PADRE
ADE MAI
PED ASSESS
ENFORCEMENT
SCORIA IGOR
 ERROL TOBY
```

Puzzle 61

```
LAGER  SETI
ARETE ETHEL
TOTEM THETA
EAT ADO WHY
 ONION HEM
STONE HORA
ATHOS GALEN
BREN METED
RIP CONES
APO AWE TEE
DEIST ROOTS
ERNIE ARRAS
 STAR LEYTE
```

Puzzle 62

```
SIDE  PILE
IDEAL ATILT
ELATE LEVER
NET MOE EVI
ASHLAND FAT
 IONE TOTO
BANDS LOREN
RIVE DIRT
ERE TEETHED
ARN IND ERA
SAINT ELDER
TICAL READE
 DENE EYED
```

Puzzle 63

```
CALL  BEGOT
OGEE SELENE
ROAD TATTLE
ORR FOR TEI
TANKARD HAH
 TERM REVE
 CHER LUKE
CHEN LIEN
HAT BONDAGE
ERR ERE CAN
ELATED SKIT
RIDERS TOTE
SEEDY  AFER
```

Puzzle 64

```
TACT  CODED
ALOUD ATONE
FLUTE SONGS
TAL FAT TRI
 DRIVE GAR
SCALE LIVE
CHASE SAVED
LORE WESER
IVE VOLTA
MEL INE DEB
ALEUT CRATE
TESTA TAROT
EDSEL  ENNA
```

Puzzle 65

```
SAKE  MATH
WRIT OLEIC
ETNA TANGLE
DUG WIT HEL
EROSIVE MAD
 FINE HAVE
FATTY BOYER
ACHE HASP
UTE SANTAFE
SOR CID TIM
TROWEL ARNO
SAONE COAT
 DEED ELLE
```

Puzzle 66

```
MERE   POSTS
AMOR  ASTUTE
SMUG  LAUREL
HEL PIG  NEV
REFINE  TRE
 TONG CHER
 STAG COED
TEEM  TILT
RAW  DENTAL
ETH REE BAD
STEPIN ELBA
SLEEVE LEER
ELDER  ISLE
```

Puzzle 69

```
PAUSE  SHEAR
IDLER  TULLE
TAMMANYHALL
    SOL  NEY
POSTURED
ADHERE  ATLE
REINE  STEED
ARNE  STERNE
   THIRDMAN
ODA  OLE
PARTYLEADER
ARIEL  TRITE
LEDGE  STEEP
```

Puzzle 67

```
LIARA  STAB
ATAR  ARMOR
MRSMALAPROP
PIE LAD ETA
ADMIRE  DAP
  ANY  HOTE
HARTE COMER
AREA  PAL
RAG  LANDED
ERA AID LOA
MALAPROPISM
TERSE  ITEM
DEED  PESO
```

Puzzle 70

```
CHAN  SCAR
LUTE  ARMOR
AMOR  LOOTED
DEMONIC  AVA
   INK  REG
MOLINE  SING
EVOKE  STAGE
NEVE  TEENER
ARE  GET
GAB  ERASMUS
ELOPER  CORE
LASSO  ALGA
 TIER  DEEM
```

Puzzle 68

```
CAFE  MANGER
AMOY  ARIOSE
BARE  DEPOTS
ART LEA DUE
LAUDER  CLAN
 NANA  HURT
 PETE  LACY
SATE  BASK
HUED  AMECHE
ULL BRA HEN
TILLER LAST
UNEASE ERSE
PERSON OMER
```

Puzzle 71

```
SPAR  ROAM
CAFE  ERIE
ARTY  CARTEL
BEE BAT EXE
RHONE  OPA
LATENT TRIP
ASHEN SHORE
SHED  SAILED
COS  CHINO
ART LAD GET
REOPEN SIRE
READ  ASSE
MARY  ITEM
```

Puzzle 73

```
CAPE   TEETER
AVON   AVERSE
MAUD   CARATS
EIN ROD  CHI
OLDTIME  KED
   FALA DATE
SCORE  HONED
TORT   DEED
EMP  TEARFUL
APO ELL  LISA
MAUMEE  TEAM
ERNEST  ALGA
REDATE  ODER
```

Puzzle 74

```
FLOP   BASIS
LANE   BEGONE
AMEN   AMANDA
SIN FRA  SIL
KAISER  SATE
  GLEE  ANER
SHED   LIDS
SETE   CALL
TASK   ASSORT
ELIT ASH VIA
LIABLE  FENT
LONELY  ERSE
ANDRE   USER
```

Puzzle 75

```
PARA   MASHER
LIEN   INHALE
ALAI   LEADEN
TEC OLT  IVE
ADHERE  STAG
  TRET  LUTE
CHOL   PIPE
SHED   PINT
TALE   ANGORA
ERI FRA  HOG
ELMIRA  MESA
VEINED  ERIN
ESTATE  LENA
```

Puzzle 76

```
SATE   ASPEN
ALATE  VERSE
LIKEN  ELITE
AVE TIR  SOD
DENTIST  ORE
  PERT  ENID
CREE   TAEL
RAIN   GARR
ASS  CANNOLI
ITO HIA  FEN
SINAI  TOWNS
ELEME  ELATE
SERIF   TROT
```

Puzzle 77

```
MASER  START
ELUDE  LOSER
TIRES  OLIVE
EVE TOP  TEA
SEASIDE  ORT
  SAVE  MUSE
PASTE  RAGED
ACHE   ROSH
LEO  SHUTTLE
OTO TON  TIM
MOTOR  DOONE
ANITA  EMBER
RENEW  REEDY
```

Puzzle 78

```
SACO   SCAM
PLAN   POLAR
EIRE   RUINED
ACT  CAPTIVE
KEEPON  PEL
  ERG   SLAV
DRAPE  STELE
RAVE   TOA
ATE  ENGAGE
MINCING  LAM
ANGORA  DIVE
GETON   EVER
RENT   RELY
```

Puzzle 79

```
PESO   STAG
RAPT   POLAR
ASIA   REINER
DEN LID  GNU
OLDMEN  ALEM
  LANG  SEGO
ARETE  RISER
MALE   SADH
AGED   ATEASE
RIG IVE  NIB
ANGORA  OKRO
GETON   KEEN
DENT   EDDY
```

Puzzle 80

```
ACHE  PAWL
SHIRR ALOES
PATIO TERNE
SIR OCEANIC
 NORMAN TEE
 CHEW POND
SAKER SLATE
ABBA DIOS
MAO  SEETHE
ALTHORN AMI
ROTOR NADIR
ANOSE ATOLE
EMER  AWED
```

Puzzle 83

```
SALES TAPS
ABOVE ARRET
LOREN STARE
ODD ASTAIRE
NEB TOY SAN
  ETON METE
ASPER MITER
TURN  MOTH
ERA SAD EVI
AVIGATE LEN
SISAL SHORN
EVENT TERSE
 EDGY ORDER
```

Puzzle 81

```
SATE CHASER
PLUM REMOVE
AIRE ONEMAN
DEN DOC EDE
ENTWINE LEG
 SHIES HIDE
  ELT YAK
SAHL CALEB
EVE SALLIED
REA PRE TRI
INTERN CHAN
AGORAE HOTE
LENITY ITER
```

Puzzle 84

```
LIRI  RABID
ADELA ABUSE
DIALS TERSE
DOT HEADSUP
 MARCEL TIE
   EAR WYNN
 THEN HANG
 LEEK TON
ERA VERDUN
ARRAIGN NAB
DEIST ELITE
ENNEA TOTAL
REGAL DELL
```

Puzzle 82

```
SANA AMASA
AGOG RECORD
MARE ASTUTE
ANT ART TIL
RAH BAA HEE
 TILT BEST
SCONE FORTE
ALAN MOON
HEL MOO BAR
AMA OLD ERA
RESTON PLOD
ANKARA ELSA
 TAPER PEER
```

Puzzle 85

```
CLOD  SHAM
ROMA MODUS
ARAD IMARET
MONEYLENDER
  SER EPI
CHUTES TRAP
HONOR DIEGO
OSSA SEARED
OTE  SHE
SETTLEDDOWN
ESTHER OLEA
SLIER FEAR
 ESPY FORD
```

Puzzle 86

```
CLEW  PEN
HULA  ALEGAR
ARID  REVIVE
RID ROMANTIC
 DEFILE GAT
   RAE VETO
BAGEL  RARER
ELLE  TEL
APA  BREEZE
KINDRED  INA
ENDRUN  CLAD
RESENT  ACRE
  WOE  THEN
```

Puzzle 87

```
CHAT  SALT
LALA  CLUES
ELIA  ROTATE
ELA  PINETAR
 ESCAPE ITO
   ART AMID
CHANT  PIECE
HOLE  POD
ELL  FINERY
ELOPING  EAT
REVOLT  MEMO
REPEL  EVER
  RETE  TENT
```

Puzzle 88

```
SANA  CLOUD
ODOR  LINNET
BABA  EVADER
EGO AVE  EPE
RED DER  REA
  YEAR  TEST
STORM  MEATY
LONE  PEAS
ERE MAD  YAP
ERA OWE  SIA
VERMIN  LAST
ENTIRE  EINE
 THREE  GLEN
```

Puzzle 89

```
SAGA   RACE
EGER  REPAST
ROTA  ASTUTE
ERA VIE  SHE
 ARTIST  TET
   IONE RITE
WASTE  LYCEE
ALEE  SEAR
IBO  RENNET
TAU IDE  MIL
ENTICE  DAME
RIOTER  IRON
 AFAR  OKRA
```

Puzzle 90

```
BARED   SLIM
ADELA  POISE
DAILYDOUBLE
ERN TAL  EEK
   FILLER
SALAMI  MATE
ARETE  BETEL
WAVE  PANELS
  EDWARD
SAR ERR  WOW
ADAYATATIME
LAGER  GAVEL
TMEN  EXERT
```

Puzzle 91

```
FADED  MORAL
ASIDE  ORONO
CHOOSENOTTO
TYR PAT  HEP
   MISER
DONATE  HEAD
ADORE  SINGE
DOWN  LINDEN
  EMILE
RUM ERE  ETA
UPAGAINSTIT
LOREN  CHARE
ENEMY  EATEN
```

Puzzle 92

```
MALI   CACHE
IDOL  MASHES
CASE  ASSORT
AGE BIT  POA
HESTON  SPIT
 ORNE  PINE
 SNEE  WINE
STEN  GONG
TEST  ARABLE
REH AME  LIA
OLEATE  MOSS
DEARLY  ACLE
EDDIE  EKED
```

271

Puzzle 93

```
MACH ALOHA
ACHE MORASS
SOIL INCITE
ARA ACE LON
INN PER ERD
 GEE  ASIE
MAKER SHEAR
ARAL  HAL
NOI ASA ASP
DUC RUM SHU
ASHORE ISAR
NEEDED SIRE
SKATE MEDE
```

Puzzle 96

```
MEIR TRIPE
OGRE RECANT
AREA ELAPSE
TEM PAY ALE
TEBET CHAT
MANY REVE
ROBIN GOMER
EVER PANI
TERN OMENS
ARM CRY GEE
IMARET AWRY
LAMINA NAVE
NATAL DYED
```

Puzzle 94

```
PASSE SEDAN
ALLEY ALIVE
CLOSESHAVES
TYE LEA ART
  HEART
SPRAT ARRAY
HEAT  EASE
ENTER RABAT
  DEPOT
SAD EAT APT
CLIFFHANGER
AERIE TORTE
DETER ERASE
```

Puzzle 97

```
SPENT SHEER
ALTER EAGLE
CANDIEDYAMS
ONA EVA DOT
  TRITE
MOOR LEVITY
ARDOR DONEE
REDTOP KENT
  HORSE
ISH SOT PIP
SWEETPOTATO
LARGE RAVEN
ENDOR EMERY
```

Puzzle 95

```
BRIG  WIN
RUSE ATABAL
ECHO TENACE
SHA GEM CHA
TELLER SKIN
LEES  CANT
RARER TANGO
EMER  GOLD
PETS REEFER
ARU SED OLA
SCRAPE TRAY
TENDON OTTO
 ATE THEN
```

Puzzle 98

```
OWE  BITT
PRIMA ASHER
EATEN STERE
ETH GEE MEN
REGALED ANT
 OREL MICA
TROTS PANEL
REDS  TALC
ING BUTTOUT
BER RIT UNE
AWARE ORRIS
LACET NESTS
 LEFT BEE
```

Puzzle 99

Puzzle 100

Puzzle 101

Puzzle 102

Puzzle 103

Puzzle 104

Puzzle 105

Puzzle 106

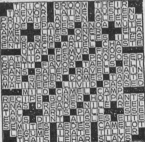

Puzzle 109

Puzzle 107

Puzzle 110

Puzzle 108

Puzzle 111

Puzzle 112

Puzzle 116

Puzzle 113

Puzzle 117

Puzzle 114

Puzzle 118

Puzzle 115

Puzzle 119

Puzzle 122

Puzzle 120

Puzzle 123

Puzzle 121

Puzzle 124

Puzzle 125

```
OILS  SETUP EASEL PLOW
EDIE  ERATO NIOBE LANE
TOMB  WATER TRIBE ASTA
ALBANESE  TRI  LEWISTON
   SOL  TRICE  DART
PASTEL DEAFENS YARROW
ORTOL REMIT TAD NOISE
SEUS  TEMPT PELEG NAME
SAMPLE TRILL PELICANS
   OATS  ALOOF  SLEW
ARRASENE OSTEO ECTYPE
SHE TRITONS ADORE PAM
PICT STOA STORY GRUB
ENURE ENE SPUS GEESE
NEREID SISTERS CEE
   AREA NOLLE SCANT
PRESENTS COL CAMELEER
AINU ILLIAC EMOTE ENDO
IGOR SALSE ROMAN STAB
RASE ESTER STENT TOME
```

Puzzle 126

```
COWL SHAUN TORAH AWOL
AMTE HARTE OVOLO PITA
WINDJAMMER WINDPLANTS
  LINER TIERS SEDUM
SPADES REDEEMS DEPART
POSES SPUNS DOIS SANER
AES CASTER STRATA LOI
RESUMES ERANS BARLEYS
  TIAA  DOR  GAY
COWARDS HAGAR BEDEWED
EDIT TETHER GENERAL TA
DINT ROIL GNEU SASSOW
ANDES PEOR GNEU CADGE
RESENT STETTED RAISES
  INERT SPURT CATCH
SAG EYAS ONE KATE IOS
WINDROWERS WINDERMERE
ANAY UNITE EMEE ALLA
MULE TYRES DIETS EDEN
```

Puzzle 127

```
YOYO SARAH DARTS SPAS
AVER IMAGO ELIOT YELL
LEAD TULIS POTSY RATE
  RACES SOWES HIRED
TAIA RAS MOOD SAR MEM
URGENT SETARIA CABALA
BEARS CATCH VISA MANET
ANTI ALLAH PASTA NAME
STICKBALL PEN OLDMAID
  RISE  TAG  TOLD
STATUES CAN POGOSTICK
HIDE SITAR BARET ALAI
ALIATE COP SLUMS PRINT
REPELS PREMISE LANATE
EST GAS IRENE SUN DOS
  JACKS RED ROVER
BOLAR ATITA MALL LEVER
USED STEIN ALLAY BADE
FANE HEARD NIECE ERIN
FRED ESMES SIDES LATE
```

Puzzle 128

```
CHOW  SAMOS
LORE  SCRAPE
ARAN  PRATED
PANDORA  ERI
   LIP  REL
  ADOPT ZITI
ANODE  REATA
TIME  SULLA
ASI  BED
LEN  AVERAGE
OTIOSE  ARAD
STOLEN  MITE
SENAL  ADEN
```

Puzzle 129

```
CLAD  OMEGA
RAGE  RECORD
AMEN  ASHORE
BIN ACH DAG
 ATOL  AMIR
   VOE  CAGE
TAPER  DUNNE
ADAR  SOT
GOTT  EMEND
ORA ACE OAF
UNMADE  ZONE
TEARED  ANTE
 DRONE  PEEL
```

Puzzle 130

```
CASTE  HADES
ALTOS  AROSE
START  SAUTE
TAB  HOP  BUN
RIISEN  SLAT
 NATE  HERO
ATLE  MACY
ASHE  BARR
STEM  ARDOR
SOB  CHI  SEL
ERATO  NISEI
NICER  ELEVE
TAKEN  SIREN
```

Puzzle 131

```
CHEW  SPAR
HOSE  CLEAR
EMPTYHEADED
REY  SEB  IDE
  SEME  ARE
FIACRE  ATOM
INTO  DOSE
ACHT  SCARED
SHE  MIAN
CIN IMP  IRA
ONIONPOWDER
GAVEL  OLEA
 NARY  WELD
```

Puzzle 132

```
HANSA  MISS
AMAIN  ASHES
HAVEINSTORE
ARE LOT WET
   MIT BENT
 SCONE ORAL
STONE CRETE
PANT PANDA
ERSE  URE
ECT ONA SOT
CHAINSMOKER
HENCE ELITE
STIR  LEMAY
```

Puzzle 135

```
HALO REGARD
AGAR OLIVER
ROMA SALINE
ERA RIT ADA
MARLINE TIM
   ETA PONY
 JENA BERG
 LUNA SON
ASH CONTACT
ITA RAY SAW
DINNER RILE
INCOME IDLE
NEEDED MEAD
```

Puzzle 133

```
CHAD  CRIB
HOME  HEART
ALOR INNEED
PENNAME VEE
   BEE INA
PREMED BAAL
REVEL SERGE
ETAT SLAYER
AIL SHA
CRU TEMPEST
HEATER ALTO
ETHER SION
EELY  TAPE
```

Puzzle 136

```
RAID  ERA
ELSE  TRACT
SEEN ROBERT
TART EDITOR
  ANNE AWE
FASTED TEA
ASTER SMELT
UTE PRISSY
COW GOIN
ERASER EDAM
TIRANE RAVE
ADDED AMON
SET  LEND
```

Puzzle 134

```
CHORE  ARM
LOVER  POET
EVADE PLAIT
WET PALTRY
 REPEAL PAL
  OWN SIDE
CLONE CHEER
HAND BOO
EVE HUNTER
LISBON LIID
ASTEL ASIDE
HALE LODGE
RAY BREED
```

Puzzle 137

```
CAPE  SALAD
AMUR GENERA
ROTA ENTAIL
TRI WESER
 NOISE NEB
SETTLE MALL
AVOID MELBA
LEES MILLET
ARF VIISTA
 FLINT BAD
ATEASE ROPE
RECTOR OUSE
ENTER ITER
```

Puzzle 138

```
MAMA  URUS
ALATE PASTE
PIKER STERN
LEE RAE DIT
ENTRANT FAR
 HUNT HOTE
SCENT PUREE
WAFT  BANC
IMU  BURGESS
PER ODA UNA
ELFIN DUPIN
SOLON ELOPE
 TYNE  ANER
```

Puzzle 141

```
HARE  GRASS
AGED  EARNED
HAVEINSTORE
ANE ODE RIN
 ATONED TAI
  TIR FETE
BASIC CORES
ERIC  SHO
AME SLIDER
REG CUE RAI
UNITEDFRONT
PINING EDGE
 AGATE DEEM
```

Puzzle 139

```
CAID   STAR
ANNE  HEATER
TIME  ARGALI
ELI DUG SED
REDWINE NAG
 PEAT BASE
CORAL DRIED
AVON  BEAL
REG TRANSOM
ERR EIN PRE
ELEVEN DADA
RISING ICER
 ESPY  NERA
```

Puzzle 142

```
HAMA  AMARA
AVOW  RIMER
RILE  IMPART
ELA ASE CEE
MARRIED HAP
 ANN PURE
MARIE LAPSE
ELON  PER
AMA CONTACT
NER HIT DAW
TRITON BODE
 INERT URGE
AGREE DEED
```

Puzzle 140

```
SOBER TEPEE
ISERE ARRAN
LINED BREST
LED WEB SIR
 ROSILY SEE
 NANA FUSE
METE  CART
ROSE  BORE
ESS RENEGE
PET ART RAW
ELEMI AGORA
ALPEN COULD
TESTY TAPES
```

Puzzle 144

```
LAID   MONO
OBOE  MADAME
LENE  OLDMEN
ADAMANT ELT
 BEY  LER
 CRUET METE
CHEST TASTE
RACE  CURSE
ERR   SAN
AME TRANSOM
TIARAE ALSO
ENTITY SOSO
GENE  HEAR
```

Puzzle 143

```
BABE  ASHE
ONYX  SHEARS
RIFE  TEEVEE
ISO REA EME
SERRIED WIN
 COOP MOTT
CHEAT VIREO
LEON  MIND
ELF PELISSE
ALA LAE WAN
VERNAL HIND
ENMITY OTTO
ESTE  THAW
```

Puzzle 145

```
DOAB  RASP
ALLER UNWED
VIDEO STERE
IVE BESIEGE
TENABLE TOP
  LEA PELE
DOVER HONAN
EPIC  HOR
PEN RENEWAL
ONETIME OLA
SIGIL SCRAP
ENARE TASTE
GREY  PEEL
```

Puzzle 148

```
CASE  ASHER
ABOVE STOLE
ROMAN HUMAN
ODE GAY ETE
NEWMAN SIG
 HAGAR WOE
CRETE AMEND
LER  DONEE
ACE  PORTER
ILE LEV HIE
MULLA ERODE
ESSED RIMED
DEEDS AERY
```

Puzzle 146

```
TAME  RODE
IDOL REPENT
TART INSIDE
ONO BAT FOR
VANDINE IRE
  ORT BEST
POUND MEDEE
LURE  TAA
ERG WRINKLE
ASE HIN NIX
SONNET CANT
ENCORE AVER
GYRE  RENA
```

Puzzle 149

```
BEGET SAMOS
ALIVE CRAPE
LIVER RATED
LAE RAE URI
 AWARE REL
 ENACT SETI
AMORE COTTA
RIPE FATHA
ANI FATSO
BEN RYE UBI
INIGO RAGED
SCOOT ETHEL
TENTH RATTY
```

Puzzle 147

```
CAFE  LOGE
AMATI IRONS
MILAN BOOTH
EEL DER URE
 ISERE TER
 SNEER SOAR
BATED LEFTY
ATOM DERBY
RIP SETTO
TAL LET USE
ETAPE ENNUI
RECAP RIDER
DENT  ESTE
```

Puzzle 150

```
SEND  MASER
ALOE BEGONE
LIVY ALEUTS
ETE ARE THO
MELANGE HUR
  LEE TEST
RICER HAYES
EVOE  HOT
LON ROSEBUD
ARC EVE ONE
PIERCE COIF
SERIAL ANTE
ESTOP PEER
```

Puzzle 157

```
SALAD MISER
EVERY ENARE
LADEN LATEN
FIG ADO AME
 LESSEN NIG
  ATE MITE
BECKY RACED
ELLE TAM
MAE ARMADA
UTA NEB ALL
SINAI LEVEE
EVENT ELITE
DERNA RADAR
```

Puzzle 155

```
CEDE BEGEM
OARED ADELE
AGILE TOTAL
LEV COE ITA
 REWARD NIN
 NANA HONG
CRUST TINGE
LAPP MARE
APA LATEST
PAW LOT HAM
PLATA LEASE
ELLEN ELITE
ROLLO FRET
```

Puzzle 152

```
GLUM BESET
LOSE SERENE
ORAN HEARTS
BRR VAT VET
 EMBERS IRA
 YORK SCOT
PARRY KEENE
ABET TEAM
LAS HELLAS
ALE EAT NEW
DORCAS RUNE
INVADE EASE
NEEDY FLED
```

Puzzle 156

```
FAIL SPEAR
ENNA ILLBET
ANTE MOTIVE
RAH NIT DEE
 EMIL BERN
 EDUCE ROSE
ELITE BONER
LEST COWED
ACTS HANS
PTA SAT TER
SINFUL DIVA
ENCASE OMEN
 GETAT TENT
```

Puzzle 153

```
DANA ASHER
ELITE SHALE
LITTLEWOMAN
LER ATA ITE
 NOTION TIIG
  INN RIVE
BRINE DICED
RENA HOT
OPT TENANT
ARE ERA AIM
DINNERTABLE
ESSEN ERODE
NEEDY ABET
```

Puzzle 154

```
LAOS CARP
ABRA ABELE
SELFEVIDENT
STEELED ATA
  LIE SEN
 LAPIN RING
DENIS PINTO
RATE DODGE
ERE BEN
ANN LATERAL
MENTALIMAGE
RAISE MIRE
 EGER ALAR
```

Puzzle 157

```
CASH AROW
LOPE SAMOS
OREL SPORTS
UTA LET DEN
TAKEON ISEE
 ONIT DOVE
PANTS REFER
HLER SHAW
APSE TULIPS
SIM SEM SIP
ENISLE IDEE
 ENTER ROTA
 DUDS AMAR
```

281

```
AMID CHAMP
LONE REPORT
TONE ENTREE
ORO SAC EPE
  TRITE DAN
 CHUTE MERE
SHINE LOSER
HENS TEPID
ERG MOVER
ARF OUI ASS
TILING ABLE
HEARTH CLUE
STAYS HEED
```

```
SAGE THECA
EGER RECORD
RITE ASHORE
ELI MIS LES
 ENSATE CAT
 HUSS BURR
SPORT BOSSY
ARTE DART
DOW MINNOW
IVA AVE MOP
SETOSE HERE
TREVOR ERSE
BRENT YSER
```

```
OSSA SCOTT
DOUR LATHES
INGE ASTRAL
SAG AVE OTA
TRESSED WIT
  SEED COME
RETEM BLUES
EMIR SEAT
MAO PENNANT
INN ACT HUR
SABINE MIRE
STORED ANSA
EXILE STET
```

```
RAPT TAMPA
ODEA ALIAS
SAAR MODISH
ERN FIN NAY
 USING TIM
 STUNG MALE
SAGES RIPEN
ATAR HUMID
NIL MEDIC
TAL ALE TEL
ATEASE PULI
ERIAN ERSE
SYRIA TEEN
```

```
ASSE HEL
LOPE ALEGAR
ALIN REVIVE
SIC SOG NID
DEEPLY GAD
IRID METE
BASIN LOREN
ELLE RASP
APA CORSET
KIN ROD ARO
ENDRUN SCAB
RESIDE OHIO
DEY TYNE
```

```
CASE PAPAL
OMIT HOARSE
MILE ERRATA
INE MAG ION
CONNERY SRO
 COST REIN
 CESS MATA
CAPE CUSH
OIL SOTHERN
ORE TUT LOI
LEAPUP TOUT
INSIDE ERSE
TEENY EDER
```

Puzzle 164

```
STRAP  SLID
HEAVE  TENET
TINCAN RANCH
POE DEA ORR
NOTARY TIO
NINE   THEN
SPENT  BRIDE
COST   REIN
ELM  LADOGA
NEO OPE FIB
ENTER  VALSE
STORE  INANE
ARAN   LITTER
```

Puzzle 167

```
ACHE   GREW
BOER   RESIST
ELAN   EASTER
TAV BED HEE
EBONY  TRA
SNORE  CHET
MACON  BLESS
ALAR   GUESS
SIN CANEA
SEW OLD ITE
ENABLE SNIP
STIRIN ETRE
TANA   ISEE
```

Puzzle 165

```
ACHE   STAB
CHAD   ARION
RARE   VENDED
END GOA YAR
OVERT  BRA
FINERY SEEP
INTRA  TEASE
ECHO   DEBUTS
SHE  SETAT
TIE EPE IVA
ANYONE AFAR
GETON  RUST
SARD   OLEA
```

Puzzle 168

```
SALAD  BLOT
AROSE  LAURA
COOPS  ASTOR
KAS ERN OPE
EARED  FIN
PRATED LOCO
RESET  PINAS
OLAN   SEMELE
WIG    TONES
LEO RUN MOW
EVOKE  ALINE
RESIN  NONCE
DENT   TIDED
```

Puzzle 166

```
HAIR   SAFER
ULNA   MALONE
MIEN   AVERTS
PAP    PREPARE
STRAND GAN
ERE    CENT
MISER  CASTS
UNAL   BON
SEL    MODEST
TRIBUNE HEW
ATEASE NANA
RINSED IRON
DATED  PERT
```

Puzzle 169

```
MOTTO  SIDE
ORAL   PRONTO
TEXASRANGER
ELI LIN RED
FIT RANI
SCRAPE EVAN
ARES   VEGA
LEST   LAUREL
AMPS   ARE
ZOO SHO FOE
ANNIEOAKLEY
RASHER EASE
ERNE   DYED
```

Puzzle 170

```
CATO   ALE
ROOT   LANCER
INTO   INDORE
BEA TEE MOP
LEANS  PSI
CHECKS ALIN
LECCE  SIEVE
ELLE   SORTED
ALI    TERSE
NEP OCA FIG
ENSATE POOR
RFELD  IONE
AME    PLAY
```

Puzzle 171

```
CAPE  TRIP
RILL  HEART
ADAM  INNEED
MAC ARE CAR
EPODE  ITO
BRAINS COIN
LEVEE PLUME
ETAT LOOSED
AIL  SOUTH
CRU CAT ELA
HEELED HAIR
DOONE  IRON
NEED  ETNA
```

Puzzle 175

```
NAPE  CASTE
ERIE  MARTEN
ROCKCONCERT
AMO ORO ARI
ATAMAN  MER
TEL  LENE
SHOT  MERE
CHOP  HEN
LOS  SELDOM
ART PRO PUP
ITALIANHERO
REGENT  ORAL
ENEMY  PALL
```

Puzzle 172

```
LINE  SAFE
ADORE ALONG
ROWEL MERGE
ALA AHA GOT
NITER  ORT
MADDEN LOGE
INFER RIDER
STOA SALADS
SER  HADON
ADE ELI DIP
LAVAL SHADE
STELE HOLES
ERIN  PLAT
```

Puzzle 176

```
CHAT  AMISS
LONE  PRONTO
ANGE  LEADEN
SOL PAT IRA
PREDATE CIT
ILE  TELA
CAMEL POSES
ABIT  HER
BAL POLECAT
ALE ERA AGA
ROAMED DUAL
ENGINE ASTO
TEENS  KEEN
```

Puzzle 173

```
AROA  CAP
PEPE  ALARIC
ALEA  SERENA
CAN SIR ASS
EXIGENT DAP
NONO  BANE
PAGAN MINER
LENT  CORD
URI COLDWAR
RAG OVA ROA
ATHOME WIRY
LETTER OTTO
OTT  WEAN
```

Puzzle 177

```
SAUL  SAW
ALGA  PLAYER
MELE  REGALE
ORY HIT NAN
STAMINA KIT
MELT  GENA
CREST CREEL
HORA  HAIG
ASI CANNOLI
SIC RIT HEN
ENAMOR LOVE
RANINE EMIR
LED  RENT
```

Puzzle 174

```
COMUS  SECT
IRATE AMAIN
TAKER BUTTE
ETE VAL CHE
ESCAPE HID
TONE WINY
CHET PING
SHED LILT
HAS SEETHE
ORC WEB ENT
OMEGA ABASE
TENOR LOCUS
READ DATES
```

Puzzle 178

```
ASSET ROWEL
RICER INANE
ENARE MERGE
NER APE NOR
AWL DID IRI
ELLA ANGE
ARTIE TIGER
DELL SELL
ACE MAR ASS
PET AIR BAT
TITAN ABELE
EVENT CALVE
DERNA EDSEL
```

Puzzle 179

```
APSE ARCHES
BAWL BEHEST
AREA AVIATE
SIE STE RUR
HATCHET TAN
NEED LORE
MORE DEFY
PATE SASH
ECH DESSERT
AHI ICH AHA
KINDER TROT
ENGAGE ETNA
DESPOT YSER
```

Puzzle 180

```
CASH FRIAR
LUPE EARLET
ORLY STELLA
TAI ETE TEN
TAPED HAN
CUSTER OESE
ONCLE CIDER
ASHE MALADY
SEE PUSSY
TAD IRA LEIT
ELUDED DOVE
RELATE UNIIT
DEBAR OGLE
```

Puzzle 181

```
ACHE BLAISE
GLAD LAMENT
RAVE ATONCE
ARI SIE ILE
ANCON HOOT
GONE ERSE
SLING RACER
TING PURL
ANSA ATTAR
BET ERA SET
AMORAL ISAR
TERESA RETE
NETTY ISAY
```

Puzzle 182

```
METED OPAH MARS ODETS
ALICE BORE ELAT CLABIA
TILTS ELAN ALDO IVORY
SALAD SID GLAIR VINES
DELICATE HAMLET
SEL MITE EME LEAR BAA
ALIMONY KNEEL ROTTERS
REMAND SNELLEN SWALES
ANIITA SHOT ENOS IRATE
HATE MOATS RATELS YES
SCENT ADITS
OST AGATES BATES CASA
SCALP REST AMOR TREED
CAPOTE RAINIER BOURNE
ALEGARS UNITS COMBINE
RED ISTS TEE TOMS EAM
SNEAKS CROSSBAR
OMAHA LATHE RES WEALS
BORAH ETUI ALTE YACAL
LITANA SEPS MOST EDILE
DENEB TRES ONES RESOD
```

Puzzle 183

```
SOPER PEARS STAIR
SALINE RADON CARTER
COLEMAN ARETE ERRATIC
ALA ATTAIN HAVANA ITO
SAAR EELS KITS INGA
ACMES DCIV PINS CRUET
SISTET ANILINE FLEERS
AERO GOING ARAN
VARIPAPA LET CREDITOR
OVEN PERIS SPARE CERO
TILE NUT AME NAB
ESSE WEBER TOPSY CETE
ROTIFE EAREAR ITERATES
DOLS SAMOS SAID
ORMOLU SAMPE STRIKE
WIELD SHAS PARR AEDES
IOTA CHAR PIER SIITS
NTA ELANDS STAPES TOA
GEMSBOK UTILE ANTHONY
DEPUTE SAVOR STEELE
RARER TREES TEMAS
```

Puzzle 184

```
CLAW RAVEN ROBIN CAPS
HEMO UTICA IRADE ALAE
IDIO ITOUS CAROU MARE
CARDINAL COE BLUEBIRD
CHER LAMBS SLUR
DEVOID WINNING ARISES
ERICS SHAI IRONE EATEN
LARK TAINT DRAKE NERI
OTE TWINGES PEARS AL
SOO THINS FREARS AMA
OAST ARAS ASIIA
TOMTIT LAKME AFIRE IRS
ILA SERINA SCALENE LET
MIRS ROMAN ALONG USNE
OVINE CAGES TOA USA AT
RESOLE SEMINAR ORIELS
WQRE RATER ARAS
REDBIRDS TEC SMALLOWS
ABRI AWETO TIOTA IRAE
ARAR TIMID ADORN NAGA
BOYD ANFLE ROPES GLEN
```

Puzzle 185

```
ARAB AFORE BLANK ISAR
BENO SARAN AERIE NINE
BECKETBEND GRANNYKNOT
EDN LUL LLEA MAYA GAS
OTATE FERNS SOTOL
CURATE RES DES NEREID
ANKLE ROS ADAH BAKRA
LINE PESO AGAPE NAG
LOO FRIARS STOKES OTO
ANTARES ACUTE FLATTEN
DIV OLE ORE
SCHOLAR ROMPS TWINKLE
PEA LIIONET SPREES NUN
ELLS LOAD ROAR NORA
ELFIN TRES DILL PETIIT
DOCTOR DEPLETE PARSEE
RAREE MOATS CORQT
AMO SAMP NIE LISA IST
HAMSERBEND CLOVEHITCH
ARNO EERIE TIIGER MCIII
BEST DRAPE STETS PHOS
```

Puzzle 186

```
RIGA CHASM MARCH SHOP
EMIL HANOI ADORE TEME
MANO SWELL IDIOM ORAN
OMAHA SLEW LLALO APART
ALBEE AAM SNARE
BGC OUR LUNAR SEE USA
LELAND BIKINIS SCALPS
AMAZE SAVES PAR ALERT
NERO EERIE KEYES EMIR
CLEVELAND WEN CHICAGO
LAGS BAN TAAS
WICHITA SAG DESMOINES
IDEIA ETHER WASTE ROLE
SIDLE EAR TINTS DARIN
POETIC SABINES BOSTON
STS DIS CUROS DIG ETA
REATA FOB VANES
ANWAR ALII RAIL SCROD
NOOK AMASA COLE RAMA
SORE METAL ALLAN AVER
ANTS ENERO KEEST PERT
```

Puzzle 187

```
ADOBE FLIAY SLAP SAMAR
LAVAL AIRA AIDA ERODE
GRAYMATTER GRAYBEARDS
AIITS THROBS ANOA MALIT
ENE GLEE OIL OLLA YES
HOAR ARGOS ALPS
HONORS ALONSOA SIEGES
OVIINE CLOU INNS ARADA
RICE PELEG NANAS AMER
ADE CALASH GRAYCOOER
SAGE NONE
GRAYRABBIIT CEMENT AAR
AIIMS NEEDY ARETE OGLE
SMOTE SEER RIN TRIAD
PARENT REACTE SALONS
MORE SNOWS BIINE
BAR SING TOR SUNK MAR
ATER ETUII TIPTOE GOBI
GRAYFRIIARS GRAYWALNUT
EILDER CROP HIKE TEASE
LAISSO EDNA TEED ANDES
```

Puzzle 188

```
FLOG CAUSE METER SAGE
LULL ALLEY ORATE ALOE
ANOA NONCE RILES IDOL
GARDENIIA SPACE TALONS
IRAS SOUSA TARO
BATONS FERNS TUBEROSE
AMOLE PINES CALLA PTS
SATI PALOS RAMIE ETON
IRE TOPER SALEP SLICE
LARKSPUR PALMS STACKS
NAPA ROSES STEN
VENERY PARIS SNOWDROP
ARIIES SEVEN FAIRS CITE
RAND ACRES DANTE CITE
ETO AGAIIN FACES BASEL
CONIIFERS REFER MIMERS
SERE DELFT LINE
REMORA SOTTO FOXGLOVE
EDAM TAIINO DOUSE LAIR
DIIRE UNGER INTER IITES
SIITAR MANET LOESS ASSE
```

Puzzle 189

```
SCAMP TACO FEUD SALSE
CUBIIO OMAN RACA TRIER
ANNAL POLEVAULT RINGO
REE EMIR SEN AURA GAD
POLEMIIC PIECE MAYPOLE
BAR TADPOLE MEL
BARON RATES ELS DEFER
ERIIN PACED SMOKE ALCO
TIAD ALIIEN PEEPING ART
ARGUMENT DONNE TRAGUS
ELIIAS PRINT CRISP
REPENT TRONA BEANPOLE
IIDO EERIEST LEANS LAR
MALL DENTS ROAST BESS
SMEAR AGE MESNE PASTE
KEN ENTIICS BOK
POLECAT DINAR POLEARM
ORA OBOL LIIP URGE LEE
LIINER TOTEMPOLE NOTED
ABEND AVER ELIAS THESE
RIISES IETS DENS AORTA
```

Puzzle 190

```
SPAT SKIIMP CANOE STLO
ARNA LAKER AGORA TRES
COAL ORATE RARER IONA
SAILBOAT SER MANOFWAR
SEPT BACON DEAF
SIIGHTS LIIGHTER DRESSY
ABRIIS VIDEO VET SNIIFE
LEAP TOADS LIIARS STOA
ERII MILNE GONDOLA ERR
SOLVED ARARA STATIISTS
IILES SKIIFF SPOT
DEMETRIIO ANSER PLACES
ELII SIGNALS MELEE ARI
GENS PIETA RABID PINO
ANIION LIIL BOLUS ORRIS
SAMPAN RADAMES CRANES
OVAL SURAS BURN
TRIIREMES RAN CORACLES
HORO INANE CLARA EARL
AMOS NILES CHESTER EDA
TIANE GNATS STORE SNOW
```

Puzzle 191

```
COBRA VIPER ADDER
DETAIN AVENS BOOMED
MARIIANA ARIES OPHIOID
ARAS ECOLES POME TRAY
NIT ROPES AURA DDE
SESS GRIT ATTEST BEER
EASCHEDE UNTIL ALARMS
HERA TIITAN ARIA
RACERS BONER BASIILISK
ADAMS PONTS SERAII RUE
BIINE KOREA CAROL LORA
BOA AIRED TOREN GENET
IISLANDER KRALT WAVERS
MIND MEETS MLLE
IMPALA MORES COLLECTIS
DAYS PLACES TELA SHOO
ENT ORCS REBA PUR
SOHO ASTA MEDUSA PRET
TROPICS STAND SINAMOS
SNATHE IIRATE ENAMOR
SLOES NIITER SENAT
```

Puzzle 192

```
FEED REPS TAAS IRIIS
PEALE ETUI AGNI NOMAD
ARGUS GALLIPOTS FABLE
GALLIINIPPER GALLIINULE
ALE RENE NEW SEED EER
PISA TUNIC YSER
REGENT ARSENIC ELOGES
ORANG GEO ETAS STARE
MILD CROUCH ERIE ALLE
AAL SHANGHAI STARTLES
ETHAN HANSA TREES
AGREEIING PENCHANT TOM
COIIN MIRE STEELS ROVE
TWERP SART TIL MONET
ANDERS BOURBON TIMERS
CEPA STAEL BESS
ASS MEMO UGH ULAM AID
GALLIICISM GALLIMAUFRY
ELIIAS GALLIIVANT TRIKE
DODGE OKIE ELAH CARES
NESS SAVE DOSE HOED
```

Puzzle 193

```
SERAC APSE ATAD OSIER
ARARA CREE RAMI SANDY
SIITAR EONS ALEC CURIE
SEEDY TUA SLUNK ARIES
AGNOSTIIC STEARO
DER RUNT ROI ANIL ATE
ULULATE KAFKA SNEEZES
MELONS REDFORD UVATES
AVERT DINE NERO ARETE
SERE SILOS SAIGON CHD
NEPAL BRETT
HAD VALETS AMBER ALBS
ARISE STET NILS CHILE
SIMILIE SNUGGLE PHONER
PALMYRA ELLES KRUEGER
SNY NICE MUL DIOR ODA
SWARDS CARAPACE
STELA EIMAK ILL HATES
PALAU ASEM SATI ISOLT
AMONG GOLI ETON LEGAL
NEIIGH ENTE TANG LLANO
```

Puzzle 194

Puzzle 195

Puzzle 196

Puzzle 197

Puzzle 198

Puzzle 199

Puzzle 200

Puzzle 201

Puzzle 202

Puzzle 203

Puzzle 205

Puzzle 204

Puzzle 206